"You Crazy Fool! You Could Have Killed Us Both!"

Gabrielle saved her breath for climbing the slope, knowing instinctively that she needed to put distance between them until Phel's temper had cooled down. She grasped a slender aspen sapling, pulling herself up over a large boulder, just as Phel's hand grasped her ankle.

"Just wait until I get my hands on you," he threatened.

Kicking free from his grip, she scrambled over the rise, then made the mistake of turning to see how close he'd drawn. Gabe's breath was coming in painful gasps as she wheeled about, right into Phel's arms.

Before she could act, he pulled her to the ground, throwing himself on top of her. His lips descended on hers as he asserted his mastery over her. Gabe struggled to throw him off, but soon realized that her efforts were wasted. He had no intention of letting her go. And she could no longer even try to escape. . . .

LENORA BARBER

loves the state of Washington, where she currently makes her home. In fact, she has a special feeling for the entire West, and her work is heavily influenced by the wide-open spaces and rugged mountains of America's last frontier.

Dear Reader:

SILHOUETTE DESIRE is an exciting new line of contemporary romances from Silhouette Books. During the past year, many Silhouette readers have written in telling us what other types of stories they'd like to read from Silhouette, and we've kept these comments and suggestions in mind in developing SILHOUETTE DESIRE.

DESIREs feature all of the elements you like to see in a romance, plus a more sensual, provocative story. So if you want to experience all the excitement, passion and joy of falling in love, then SILHOUETTE DESIRE is for you.

I hope you enjoy this book and all the wonderful stories to come from SILHOUETTE DESIRE. I'd appreciate any thoughts you'd like to share with us on new SILHOUETTE DESIRE, and I invite you to write to us at the address below:

Karen Solem
Editor-in-Chief
Silhouette Books
P.O. Box 769
New York, N.Y. 10019

LENORA BARBER
Blueprint For Rapture

Silhouette Desire

Published by Silhouette Books New York

America's Publisher of Contemporary Romance

SILHOUETTE BOOKS, a Division of Simon & Schuster, Inc.
1230 Avenue of the Americas, New York, N.Y. 10020

ISBN: 0-671-46625-9

First Silhouette Books printing July, 1983

10 9 8 7 6 5 4 3 2 1

1

Gabrielle Seberg planted her feet in an uncharacteristically wide-legged stance, as though bracing herself against a gale-force wind, and stood her ground. She was not about to be intimidated by this man—no matter how loud his bellow of rage or how menacingly he waved his arms.

"Mr. Cannon," she said, silently cursing the fact that she was forced to look up to meet angry eyes as blue and bottomless as the lake at her back. "You and I have a contract and I intend to hold you to it."

A face that could have been molded expressly to portray the scorn it now held looked down at her in dismissal. "I signed a contract with Gabe Seberg of Ponderosa Rustic Homes for the construction of a custom log home on this island." His eyes raked over her delicate, sweetly molded face and soft feminine form. "I never agreed to put out more than two hundred thousand dollars for some emancipated kitten to play house with *my* house!"

The words brought fire to Gabrielle's wide-set, normally tranquil hazel eyes. Sparks of gold and green appeared to enlarge the dark brown outer ring, and her pupils became tiny black dots in the bright sunshine. Two pink spots of color rose to her cheekbones.

"Mr. Cannon," she said with a vigorous shake of her short sandy-colored curls. "I don't care what your personal opinion of one-half of the human race might be! I can only ask you to not lump me with everyone you've had a bad experience with and consider me as an individual."

"A female individual!"

"This isn't the first time I've met with resistance to the idea that a woman can be a competent builder." Gabe hesitated for a moment, thinking what a sweeping understatement that was. Her background—as a contractor's kid who'd hung around building sites ever since her mother had died when Gabe was ten years old—hadn't stilled the snorts of disbelief when she'd enrolled at the Mackie School of Log Home Building in Prince George, British Columbia. And even after almost a year of studying wood-preservation techniques at the State Technical Institute near Oslo, Norway, she was still routinely mistaken for a contractor's wife rather than a qualified builder in her own right.

In fact, her wish to avoid that ingrained prejudice against women in a nontraditional field had prompted her to commission an estimating firm to negotiate the contract on the Cannon job after she had compiled the bid herself. Until she'd arrived at Wild Stag Island, Phel Cannon's only contact had been with the salesman from Spokane, Washington, who'd acted on her behalf.

Gabe thrust her hands into the hip pockets of her jeans, unaware of the way her breasts thrust provocatively forward under her shirt. After seven hours in the old truck that she always used to haul the portable generator to a job site, her clothes clung damply to every womanly curve. Gabe's mind quickly sorted through ideas, seeking an approach that might appeal to Phel Cannon's business sense.

"Look," she said a bit more reasonably, "I've already invested your entire advance in building materials and spent most of the profit from my last job on the excavation subcontractor, not to mention the amount I paid for the salesman's commission."

She gestured patiently toward a mammoth pile of neatly stacked logs alongside pallets of plywood and cut lumber. "The materials were delivered to the site before June first—as specified in the contract," Gabe went on. "Before the snow flies you will be the proud owner of a custom hand-crafted log home that will still be just as beautiful a thousand years from today."

Gabe reminded herself that her father had always told her that she could catch more flies with honey than with vinegar. "It's too late for me to rearrange my schedule." She flashed him a winsome smile. "My crew will be here in the morning."

"I don't care if the devil himself will be here

7

tomorrow!" he thundered. "I've spent the entire first year of my retirement designing this house and I'll be damned if I'm going to let a woman build it!"

"Mr. Cannon," Gabe said, thinking that the devil himself was already here, "you needn't shout for me to understand what you're saying." She found it difficult to keep the quaver out of her voice with the threatening figure of Phel Cannon towering over her. "I've been pushing that old truck all day to haul the generator and tools from Washington to Montana.

"I'm hot and tired and I don't want to stand around on the dock any longer hashing over a moot point." In spite of her intention to be reasonable, her patience was wearing thin. "Now, if you'll just get out of my way, I'll get that truck unloaded and call it a day."

"You can save yourself the trouble. Just get back on that barge and ferry your truck and yourself back to the mainland!"

The ferocity with which he delivered the statement almost made Gabe wonder if he would resort to force. She controlled a shudder, telling herself that her slight flicker of fear had been prompted only by the remoteness of their location. They were a good fifteen miles from Polson, the nearest town, in a rugged area populated only part of the year by a few summer people. And though only two hundred yards away from the western shore of Flathead Lake, Wild Stag Island could only be reached by boat.

Fleetingly, Gabe wondered why Phel Cannon had sought such an isolated lifestyle that he'd purchased an island to insure his privacy. The research she'd quickly done before submitting her bid had revealed that Phel—short for Phelan, an old family name that meant wolf in the ancient Celtic tongue—had made a fortune in California real estate and retired the year before at the age of forty.

She hadn't looked any further into his background, since she'd been interested primarily in his financial stability. She couldn't afford to put time into estimating a bid for a project that had no likelihood of being built. It was enough of an obstacle that the house was to be constructed on an island, necessitating the use of a raft powered by twin fifty-horsepower outboard motors to ferry materials and equipment across the water.

Gabe walked across the front of the barge and lifted a ten-foot length of two-by-twelve planking, then positioned it to serve as a ramp connecting the barge to the dock. Although the raft had been constructed for this specific use, the weight of the truck caused it to sink slightly, leaving a gap of a few inches between the dock and the floating platform.

Phel Cannon continued his tirade as she returned for a second plank and slid it into place in front of the truck's front wheels. "You're wasting your time," he bellowed. "You'll unload that truck over my dead body!"

Gabrielle straightened and leveled her multicolored gaze at him, unable to conceal her irritation any longer. "As you wish," she said with honeyed sweetness. "Will you please write out a check for the balance of the contract before you go?"

The look on his face told her she'd gone too far. As he started toward her, Gabe hopped into the cab of the old truck that had hauled tools to every job for as long as she could remember. When her father had retired a few months after her marriage, she and Buddie had fallen heir to the old workhorse.

Pushing aside the twinge of bittersweet sadness that still accompanied any thought of Buddie, even though it had been more than three years since his death, Gabrielle coaxed the ancient engine to life.

Phel Cannon took a stand in front of the truck, looking as dark and craggy and insurmountable as any of the mountains around them.

Gabe's hands were sweaty on the steering wheel as she felt the tires grip the plank and crawl onto the dock, which was barely wide enough to accommodate the truck. She gritted her teeth in determination as she continued her course until she actually brought the bumper against the knees of the man who stood defiantly, refusing to let her pass.

Gabe revved the engine in warning, sure he would move aside before she let out the balky old clutch. The truck lurched forward, but Phel stood his ground until the last possible moment. When her determination finally registered in his mind, it was too late for anything but reflex action.

Sheer terror gripped Gabe when she heard the splash. Now she'd done it! She'd only meant to show him that she couldn't be bullied around! She turned off the engine and jerked on the handbrake, leaving the old truck still rocking on its tracks when she hit the deck.

Worry over whether she'd actually hit Phel or if he had jumped out of the path of the lumbering vehicle drove her to the edge of the dock. She bent down and extended a hand to help him back to the dock, but, dashing aside the proffered hand, he merely brushed the water from his streaming eyes. Then he appeared to reconsider her offer of help.

So great was Gabrielle's relief that he was all right, she forgot his animosity in her eagerness to help him. His steely grasp had already locked around her wrist when she realized that he intended to take revenge for his dunking. She caught only the briefest glimpse of satisfaction in his eyes as she came tumbling toward him. It was almost a relief to escape his gloating look of revenge when the water closed over her head.

She opened her eyes, recoiling at the icy sting of the lake. Above her she could see the sunlight filtering through the murky water with a strange green light. As she struggled to propel her leaden body upward it took her an instant to figure out that Phel had wrapped one arm around her and was towing her to shore. She tried to fight free of his hold, but her struggles only seemed to make the contact more intimate.

A moment later, as he deposited her unceremoniously in the shallow water lapping the beach, he threw himself down on top of her. His face was only inches above her own, his breath as labored as hers.

Incensed, Gabe refused to yield as his eyes demanded submission. Suddenly she was desperately aware of the pressure of his long, lean body against her own feminine softness, too actively conscious of the masculine mouth that suddenly softened with passion as it hovered only inches above her own softly parted lips. She was so overwhelmed by the compulsion to taste the sensual promise of those lips that she tried to roll away, and was startled at the sensation of waves lapping in her ears when she sank back a little. With a jerk she raised her head again, straining to hold the awkward position, all too aware of his arousal and wondering what he planned to do.

His kiss, when it came, was surprisingly gentle—reassuring almost—a marked contrast to the barely leashed passion she had expected. Her own response was puzzling. A part of her screamed in protest, but, at the same time, her senses reeled from the impact of the promise of ecstasy his mouth was imprinting on her soul.

The kiss deepened. It seemed to Gabrielle that she had known those hungry lips all her life. The message they stamped on her own tender mouth spoke of the same recognition.

After an eternity he lowered a knee to the muddy lake bottom and pulled her upright. With what dignity she could muster, Gabe got to her feet and sloshed to the bank. Her hair was plastered to her head and water trickled from her heavy leather work boots as she walked. The weight of her muddy, water-laden jeans made her steps seem hopelessly weary.

Phel Cannon made a detailed survey of her heaving breasts, outlined in exquisite detail by the clinging and dripping yellow tee shirt, as she pulled pieces of water lily stems from her matted hair. She glared back angrily until she became aware just how much her upraised arms enhanced the contours that he was studying so closely.

She dropped both her arms and her eyes, looking down in confusion at her hands. It seemed incongruously funny to discover that one held a rather muddy and bedraggled lily.

Her laughter might have been nothing more than an instinctive attempt to keep from crying, but when it burst into life, echoing back from the rocky fortress of the island, even the angry man at her side was forced to see the humor in the situation.

A smile split the granite lines of his face, rearranging the hard-hewn angles into a pleasant boyishness. "I guess since I almost drowned you the least I can do is let you come up to the cabin to clean up," he offered. "Do you have a bag in the truck?"

"I'll get it," Gabe said, thankful for the opportunity to regroup and marshall her scattered composure. It was a relief to get away from him so she could think more clearly.

As she climbed into the truck to retrieve her duffel bag, she was tempted to head back to civilization—back to where there were no prowling, dangerous savages to fear.

But she hadn't gotten to where she was now, owner of her own construction company at the age of twenty-nine, by running away from adversity. At no time during the past three years had she been free of the struggle to prove her capability. She had had to prove her abilities to her own crew and she was prepared to earn Phel Cannon's respect as well.

Determination was etched in every line of her

face as Gabrielle started the truck and edged it forward. After parking alongside the stacks of lumber, she grabbed her bag and strode purposefully up through the clearing after Phel Cannon's retreating figure.

Looking about for the first time since her initial glance around on her arrival, Gabe noticed a small cabin cruiser moored on one side of the dock, bobbing alongside a smaller rowboat. Just beyond the stacks of lumber were mounds of dirt and rock from the excavation for the new dwelling.

As she looked at the site for the first time, details from the blueprints provided her with an accurate image of the huge log home. It would become an aesthetic part of the environment despite its size and the scope of the sweeping deck that would actually jut out over the water's edge.

Through the trees she could see the A-frame cabin that was presently the only building on the island. Tucked away in a sylvan setting of overhanging pine boughs, the cabin appeared to be little more than a hunting or fishing hideaway.

As she approached it she was just in time to see Phel kick off his soft-soled loafers and drop his saturated demin pants about his ankles. He kicked them aside without any pretense of prudery. After dropping his shirt on top of the jeans, he bent to turn on a garden hose, adjusting the water flow to a fine mist.

Gabe found that it took a supreme effort to keep her eyes from straying to the rippling thigh muscles and long muscular back that tapered down to a narrow waist. He sprayed the water all over himself, first washing off the mud that clung to his legs and torso, and then ducking his head to wash the tangy-smelling lake water from his curly black hair.

Only partly recovered from the shock of seeing Phel immodestly strip down to his shorts, Gabe sat down on the porch steps and unlaced her soggy boots. When a quick glance assured her that he was paying her no attention, she shucked off her dripping jeans, folded them primly and placed them on the steps.

Two can play this game, she thought grimly. If Phel Cannon had changed his tactics and was only pretending to soften toward her while he attempted to embarrass her into leaving, he had better rethink the situation.

After finishing his primitive shower, Phel turned the nozzle until only a trickle emitted from it, then offered the hose to Gabrielle. He folded his arms across his broad chest and watched her, almost as if he couldn't look away.

Gabe stood as though frozen, looking like a siren who had just risen from the mists of the lake, in her clinging tee shirt and revealing panties. Involuntarily she shivered as she felt the prickle of goosebumps rising on her flesh. She wasn't sure if she was chilled by the predatory look in Phel's eyes or by the wind that had sprung up so swiftly as the sun slid behind the mountains.

"I'll be glad to help you with that." His voice held a curious mixture of derision and interest.

"Thanks," Gabe returned wryly. "I don't need any more help from you." She gasped as the icy water struck her skin. Hurriedly, she rinsed the muck from her hair, anticipating the luxury of the shower that would follow when she got enough mud off to enter the cabin.

By the time she'd endured the icy spray as long as she could, Phel was standing in the doorway.

"You'd better come in before you catch a chill." He looked undecided, not really eager to offer his hospitality. "I'll make some tea and build a fire."

He was standing at a small sink on one side of the single room, filling a teakettle, when Gabe entered the cabin. She closed the door behind her, glad to shut out the chill of the early June evening. She dropped the duffel bag at her feet and looked around in dismay.

It was a large room with a crude rock fireplace, flanked by two easy chairs, along one wall. The kitchen area took up another wall and consisted of a few cabinets, the sink, a propane stove and a camper-sized refrigerator. A small wooden drop-leaf table and two chairs stood nearby. The single light in the room came from a Coleman lantern standing on a small desk, next to which was a floor-to-ceiling bookcase.

Gabe could feel a flush creeping up her neck and across her face as her eyes sought and found the sleeping area. A heavy chest of drawers stood at the foot of the double bed; a cheery, inviting patch-work quilt was the only object in the room with any color.

Phel turned from placing the kettle on the flame and studied his unwanted guest. "Rustic, isn't it?"

"But you . . ." Gabe's throat was so dry that she couldn't speak until she had swallowed. "You agreed in the contract to provide me with lodging for the duration of construction!"

"But you"—his twisted smile made Gabe think wildly of a sadistic cat with its paw on a mouse's tail—"neglected to inform me that you are a woman."

Her cheeks flared anew as she took in the bed, with all its implications. "But surely you didn't intend . . . I mean, even if I were a man . . ."

"There's a trundle bed underneath." He seemed to draw an enormous amount of satisfaction and amusement from her discomfort. "Since night seems to have fallen while we were playing in the water I have no choice but to suggest you use it tonight." He raised a wolfish eyebrow. "Unless you would like to try my mattress."

"I don't want to try anything of yours!" Gabe's frustration was apparent in her anguished voice. "All I want is for you to give me the professional courtesy due my training and experience until such time as I complete my contract."

"Miss Seberg . . ."

"It's *Mrs.* Seberg, please."

"Oh, is it?" Phel bowed slightly, as though having just been accorded a formal introduction, before going on. "It is exceedingly difficult, Mrs. Seberg, to grant you the dignity you say you expect when you are standing in the middle of my bedroom attired in a wet tee shirt and lacy unmentionables."

Without a word Gabe snatched up her duffel bag and strode across the cabin. She jerked open the only door in the room and, for a moment, thought she would suffer the mortification of exiting into a closet, but the small dressing area led to an even tinier bathroom with primitive plumbing.

She pulled the door shut with a bang and leaned against the frame until she stopped shaking. There was only cold water, but Gabe found the chilly water deliciously cooling on her flushed face.

She took time to do a more thorough job of washing up, realizing with disappointment that she'd have to forego the hot shower she'd longed for. Quickly she dried herself with a rough, over-sized brown towel that made her skin tingle.

Remembering the way Phel Cannon's ravenous eyes had lingered on her feminine curves, Gabrielle chose an old flannel work shirt that had once been Buddie's and buttoned it with shaking fingers.

Swiftly she drew on a pair of carpenter's overalls and was buckling the suspenders just as a sharp tap on the door summoned her.

"Tea's ready." Phel Cannon's voice sounded harsh, even through the heavy wooden door.

He was kneeling in front of the hearth, striking a match to a well-laid teepee of kindling and logs, when she reentered the room, looking anything but seductive in her bulky work clothes. Phel, on the contrary, hadn't dressed, but wore a white terry-cloth robe that barely skimmed the lithe, muscular curve of his thighs.

The tempting aroma of herb tea wafted from a cup on a small stand, luring her to the comfort of a huge overstuffed chair. A sigh she couldn't suppress escaped her lips as she swallowed the first sip and basked in the warmth of the already blazing fire.

"You make a good cup of tea, Mr. Cannon." She inclined her head graciously.

"It's one of my more commendable talents." He rose and poured himself a cup from the pot on the table at her elbow. She avoided his eyes, deliberately looking at the fire. Although at five feet, eight inches, she was not a small woman, the man next to her seemed to dwarf everything in sight, including herself.

Gabrielle lowered her gaze to the steaming liquid in her cup until he moved away. She was too aware of his nearness, too puzzled by her lack of control over her own thoughts. They kept straying back to the moments when he'd held her at the water's edge. To the kiss that still threatened to drown her in sensation.

When she'd finished her tea Gabe rose and searched her bag for a flashlight. Without explanation she switched it on and went outside, carefully making her way down the path to the truck. If she were going to survive the evening with any amount of tranquility, she was going to have to occupy her unruly mind with something other than kisses.

Phel rose to his feet instantly when she entered the cabin, lugging a large aluminum blueprint case. "I would have carried that in for you."

"Thanks, but you needn't bother." Her tone was crisp and businesslike. "I learned to carry my own case when I was in architecture school." She mentally marked a slash on an invisible scoreboard in her mind and congratulated herself on the small measure of respect that appeared on his face.

"Yes, in case you're wondering," she said with

19

satisfaction, "it *was* me who drew the improvements on your original design."

"Look, Miss . . . Mrs . . ."

"Gabrielle."

"There's a big difference between drawing plans and building a log home."

"I know; I've just completed three of them on the Colville Indian Reservation in central Washington. It was a year-long, backbreaking job."

"You may have accomplished that out on the plains, but nothing comes as easy here in the mountains. You have to dig through rocks as old as time." Phel Cannon's voice rose forcefully. "You wouldn't last a week here. This is hard, mean country! The winters are—"

"That doesn't concern me," Gabe interrupted determinedly. "I'll have the job finished and be out of here before winter comes."

"Why won't you listen to reason?"

"Whose reason? Yours?" She resisted the temptation to be drawn into a shouting match, keeping her voice well modulated and businesslike. "Mr. Cannon, I've met a lot of men who panic at the very thought that a woman might be capable enough to succeed in this line of work. I'd like to think you're too intelligent to fall into their ranks." Her eyes flickered over him, looking for understanding. "I guess I was lucky to have been raised by a father who wasn't blinded by tradition . . . and fortunate enough to have married a man who was glad to have a partner in establishing his own construction company."

"Right now I'd say it was too bad he didn't have the foresight to keep you in the kitchen where—"

"—where a woman belongs?" Phel's intolerant attitude goaded Gabe to reply. "He did. He realized that I am an infinitely more qualified kitchen designer than he was. Your own floor plans will attest to the quality of my education."

Still smarting from his criticism, she opened the case and drew forth the house plans to spread them out on the desk. Her heart still thudded fiercely inside her ribcage as she made a pretense of studying the blueprints she could have drawn in her sleep, so well did she know them.

"If your husband is a partner in the business, why isn't he here instead of you?" Phel refused to let the subject drop.

"He was killed in an accident on a job up in Canada." Her tone was matter-of-fact, revealing nothing of the pain she'd endured before she'd come to terms with that fact. "Three years ago," she added dully.

Phel stood and watched her for a moment, apparently stunned by the magnitude of his inadvertent blunder. "I'm sorry. I wouldn't have said that if I had known." He moved to the kitchen area and poured himself a drink. "Want one?" he asked, gesturing with the bottle of Scotch.

"No, thank you."

Drink in hand, Phel retired to an easy chair, propped his long legs up on a hassock and sipped slowly as he watched the woman at his desk.

For the next hour, Gabe was disconcerted to find that he was still sitting there staring at her each time she looked up. When she could bear his surveillance no longer, she rose and put the blueprints back in the aluminum case.

Phel's glittering eyes, dark and reflective now, like the lake at night, followed each move she made.

Feeling like a specimen under a microscope, Gabe crossed the room, flipped up the quilt and pulled out the trundle bed. She hesitated only a minute when the frame stopped even with the larger bed. Again she took the flashlight and went outside, returning armed with a crescent wrench and a pair of pliers. The hardware was old and slightly rusted, but she refused to give her host the satisfaction of asking for his help.

Gabe hadn't heard Phel move to her side, so she jumped when his hand closed over her own. Her fingers loosened on the wrench, surrendering the tool into his insistent hand. With a few deft motions he accomplished the task and returned the tools to her.

She mumbled an unsteady thanks and turned to roll the trundle bed as far from the other bed as space would allow.

After a few minutes in the bathroom, during which she decided to follow her normal routine rather than make a point of prudery, Gabe returned to the room clad in cool cotton pajamas of a fine green-and-white-striped percale. With a noncommittal "goodnight" she slipped into the low-slung bed and pulled the heavy quilt up over her shoulders. Her muscles were taut with tension that made it impossible for her to relax.

The fire had burned down, leaving a red glow in the room, a spark that was reflected from Phel's eyes each time Gabe allowed her own restless eyes to seek him out again. Like the glowing, iridescent eyes of a night animal lurking just outside the warmth of a campfire, they waited and watched.

In a fit of frustration Gabrielle turned her back and covered her head with the quilt. Closing her eyes tightly, she was engulfed by a feeling of emptiness that too often haunted her on such lonely nights as this when sleep was elusive. She'd long ago adjusted to the loss of Buddie—knew he would never again draw her close in sleep, entangle her in love's embrace. But she grew more restless and lonesome with each passing week.

Surely it was nothing more than a residual longing for intimacy that had caused her body to respond so irrationally to the nearness of Phel Cannon's masculine frame as they'd wrestled at the water's edge. She'd felt the same tug of arousal when he'd boldly stripped down to his shorts in an effort to embarrass her into leaving, but no doubt the reason was the same.

Such a response would be easier to understand, she thought, if he were the kind of man who appealed to her. But even that was nonsense, she reminded herself fiercely. She hadn't been attracted to *any* man in the three years since Buddie's death.

When Gabrielle had first been widowed, she had earnestly thrown herself into learning all she could about construction, knowing somewhere in her deepest heart that time and work would heal the devastation Buddie's death had wrought.

She had spent the past year out on the reservation, with every ounce of her energy going into the construction of the three log homes she'd built there. Evenings had always found her ready to turn in, a good night's sleep sounding more inviting than a long drive into town and the dubious selection of company she might have found there.

Perhaps, Gabe thought, when this job was finished she should consider going back to Spokane. It shouldn't be too hard to reestablish some old friendships, put down some roots and begin to think of the future in some terms other than career goals. As long as she continued to work in such remote locations there was little likelihood that she would change her solitary lifestyle.

It was time she faced the truth. Her clamorous response to Phel Cannon's kiss was an easily diagnosed symptom of her need for the warmth and physical satisfaction of an intimate relationship. She wasn't the kind of woman who, having once savored the oneness of a good marriage, could be content to live alone forever.

Perhaps someday soon she would experience again the sweet joy of loving a man with the same tender, caring nature Buddie had had. But that had no relation to that brief flare of recognition—of one animal instinct responding to another hungry need —she had felt with Phel Cannon.

Gabrielle turned restlessly in her sleep, pushing aside the heavy quilt. In the darkness of half sleep, glowing red animal eyes haunted her. A bone-chilling howl rent the silence. The eerie wail was followed by another and then another until the lament became a chorus.

In her half-conscious state Gabe felt as though she were surrounded by a pack of shadowy gray creatures, all nipping and growling and baying in unison. The howling grew louder until she thought the shaggy animals must be closing in around her.

Bolting up in bed with a gasp, her hand flew to her mouth. At the sound of movement a few feet away, the gasp became a scream. It was too dark in the room to see more than an outline, but Gabe was aware of a shadowy form that moved to the side of her bed.

"What is it?" she cried out. "Are they wolves? Can they get in?"

The bed sagged slightly as Phel's weight settled by her side. "You don't have to be frightened." His voice was rough, as if he'd fallen asleep in his chair only to be rudely awakened by the howling. "There aren't many timber wolves left around here," he assured her. "It's probably only coyotes."

Gabe wasn't so easily calmed. "Oh, it's *only* coyotes!" she croaked, her body stiffening in protest as Phel stretched out alongside her and threw one arm over her huddled frame.

"Maybe if I don't tell you that nothing less than a forest fire would drive them into the lake you'll be frightened enough to cling to me for protection."

"What do you mean?" Gabe asked suspiciously as she tried to draw away from him.

"They're on the mainland." He humored her with the explanation, as though he were talking to a real tenderfoot. "That's one advantage to living on an island."

"If you mean that wolves can't come here, I'd say that at least one managed to get over."

Phel shrugged patiently. "I see someone told you what my name means."

"I understand that Phelan is an old family

name," Gabe returned. "Does that mean you sprang from a succession of predators?"

Phel sighed heavily. "Ah, for ancient times! The wolf wasn't so maligned then. Perhaps you've read the legend of the she-wolf who suckled the twins Remus and Romulus, the founders of Rome?"

"Perhaps you've read the story of the wolf that ate Little Red Riding Hood's poor grandmother?"

"There, you see?" He seemed to settle back more, resting against the pillows. "Wolves have had such bad press!"

Gabrielle wanted to move further away from him, but she was pressed almost against the wall. Besides, she could still hear the howling and there was a certain comfort to be derived from his strength. In spite of her contrary intention, she found herself nestling a little closer.

Phel seemed to take her slight movement as encouragement, because he turned on his side and reached for her. Before Gabe could react, his lips had found hers in the darkness. His kiss held all the tenderness she'd noticed earlier, and so much more. Hungrily he devoured her mouth, teasing her lips until they parted to admit his questing tongue.

Gabe stiffened with shock, unprepared for the megavolts that melded her to him. A protest started deep in her throat, but somehow it was transformed into an earthy sigh by the time it escaped her lips.

As Phel explored the inner recesses of her mouth, the softness of her lips, his hands were working gently about her neck and shoulders, coaxing her to relax against him.

His long fingers gently massaged her tight muscles and stroked her soft skin, then reached under her pajama collar. His touch warmed her in a way that was as relaxing as the swirling jets of a Jacuzzi and just as stimulating.

His lips elicited an equally excited response as long breathless moments went by. His mouth moved from her parted lips to her eyes, his breath as warm as the tender caress he pressed against her eyelids.

Gabe felt a growing awareness of Phel's masculine response to their closeness and wondered fleetingly how he could be so obviously aroused and yet restrain himself to such a tender embrace. No sooner had the thought occurred to her than his embrace changed markedly.

The arms that held her were still gentle, but suddenly much more insistent. His hands were burning into her flesh through the thin fabric of her pajamas. Gabe was smitten with a compulsion to feel those rough fingers upon her skin. As though he could read her thoughts he began to unbutton the front of her pajamas, moving painfully slowly as he stopped to trace each inch of skin as it was revealed. By the time he'd reached the third button, the sensitive flesh of her breasts was aching with its need to know the feel of his touch.

When at last he pushed the garment aside he searched out a trembling mound, circling the bud with his tongue before seizing the hardened nipple with his teeth.

Moaning softly, Gabe pressed her body against his thigh where he'd thrown his leg across her. The sensation was just too delicious to move away from, even though she was vaguely aware of how dangerously near she was to a precipice where desire could easily take precedence over reason.

As Phel moved to synchronize his movements with her own, Gabe's fingers played across the roughly textured hair on his chest, then brushed lightly across the smooth skin of his back. In the darkness she realized that he still wore the terry robe he'd put on earlier, but it provided little barrier to her exploring fingers. Almost involuntarily her hands continued to move up over the powerful muscles of his back, pressing him closer still.

As though her need were only a reflection of his own, Phel shifted his weight again to bring their bodies into fuller contact, yet he was careful to not crush her with his full weight.

Gabrielle could feel a trembling in his powerful limbs. The knowledge that she had aroused him to such an extent did nothing to cool her own response. Moaning softly, she arched against him, seeking satisfaction for the rising flame within her.

Her soft moan was almost a sigh as Phel's hand pushed down the elastic waist of her pajamas. Lovingly he explored the curve of her hip and thigh before urging her closer.

Phel's lips burned into the hollow of Gabrielle's throat. "You're so warm and delectable." His voice was suffused with passion, husky and deep. "I must have been insane to try to run you off!"

The words doused Gabe's ardor as effectively as if he'd thrown a bucket of cold water over her. What was she doing? What madness had made her forget for a few exciting moments who this man was, holding her so intimately?

Roughly she pushed him away and sat up,

pulling her pajamas together in front to cover her nakedness. "So much for your claim that wolves are harmless," she said sharply. "It's a good thing I trust my own instincts; I'm not taken in by your seductive ploy."

She wished she could see his face so she could know his response. He sat up slowly and swung his legs over the side of the bed. Without a word he belted his robe about his waist. Just then a wailing howl shrieked through the silence.

"Phel?" Gabrielle's voice quavered, sounding like that of a frightened child. "That creature sounds like it's right outside the door."

"So which wolf frightens you the most?"

At her involuntary shudder he sagged heavily against the pillows, folding his arms over his chest. "All right," he growled. "But don't expect me to understand how a liberated woman like you can be so scared of a few coyotes."

When Gabe didn't reply he chuckled softly in the dark. "Go to sleep, Gabrielle. I'll stay right here by your side to protect you from all the howling night creatures."

2

Gabrielle woke slowly to the first light and sounds of a new morning. She heard the shrill scolding of chipmunks in the pines, the soft, throaty coo of a mourning dove, the strident cry of a night hawk making its last pillaging flight over the water before retiring from the morning's sun.

Throwing off the drug of somnolence, she started to turn over, but was hindered by the weight of a strong leg heedlessly thrown across her own. The arm that pinned her in position was heavy with sleep as she dislodged the fingers which still cupped a blushing breast.

Soundlessly she extracted herself from the slumbrous embrace and tiptoed into the tiny bathroom. As quietly as possible, she dressed in her working clothes, then went outside. On the porch steps she sat down and put on the tennis shoes she'd re-trieved from her duffel bag the night before.

The rising sun, hidden by the rocky rise of the island, created a glittery pathway, first gold and then brightening to silver, on the lake. The reflected light was so bright that it made Gabe's eyes water.

She didn't look up when the door behind her opened and closed. Silent minutes went by as she continued her study of the lake. The quiet was disturbed only by a vociferous exchange between two magpies.

She knew he was standing there. Indeed, her peripheral vision took in his bare feet. At length he sat down next to her. When he attempted to put his arm over her shoulder she leaped to her feet.

"Gabe . . . Gabrielle . . ."

She wasn't ready to cope with his nearness. Wasn't ready to accept the realization that her indiscretion had placed her in an intolerable posi-tion.

"If it's all right with you, I'll make some coffee and then I'm going to take the raft over to shore." She deliberately avoided any reference to what was hanging between them, threatening to overwhelm her if she acknowledged it. "The crew will be there with the camper trailer by eight o'clock."

"Gabe . . ." Phel grasped her shoulders and pulled her around to face him. "What is this?"

"I don't know what you mean," she told him in a frosty voice.

"Then it's time for us to get some talking done."

"We've already done our talking. If you want to try to break the contract I suggest you see an

31

attorney. Until then, I intend to deliver on my part of the agreement—and to hold you to yours."

"But last night . . ."

"Forget about last night! It was an accident!"

"An accident!" he repeated incredulously. "An accident is something that hurts someone. You can't take something beautiful and just deny it . . . pretend it never happened."

"Funny, that's exactly what I intend to do." Her voice was flinty, like the glittering mica of the sharp pebbles on the beach. "Whatever your purpose was, you wasted your effort."

"Purpose!" Angrily he shook her, his fingers biting into her arms through the coarse flannel sleeves. "Damn you!"

Gabe's hazel eyes were a torment of self-reproach. "Mr. Cannon, please take your hands off me."

"How can you talk so coldly when you were melting in my arms a few hours ago?" Suspicion gave an ugly twist to his mouth. "Or was that all just contrived so I'd allow you to stay here?"

"*Allow* me?" she demanded. "You should have thought about whether you wanted a stranger camping with you *before* you accepted my bid."

"Forget about the damned house for a minute." He loosened his grip, but still didn't let her go free. "What about last night? You can't pretend you weren't aroused."

It was true. She couldn't deny her response any more than the morning could deny the arrival of the new day. But nor could she confess her vulnerability to him—or she would find it impossible to stay here on the island for the next three months.

Even if it destroyed the fragile truce they seemed to have negotiated the night before, she had to free herself of the bonds an intimate relationship with Phel Cannon would impose on her.

Her reply was spiteful, a last-ditch effort to evade the truth. "You mustn't take that personally." She almost cringed as she said the words. "I told you, I've been alone for three years."

The patronizing words had their desired effect. He shoved her roughly away and strode to the end of the long porch, only to turn and stride back again threateningly.

"Do you know what I'd like to do to you?"

"Mr. Cannon, why don't you just forget about what you might like to do to me and kindly tell me where you keep the coffee?"

Elmer and Turk were waiting on the far shore when Gabe guided the ungainly raft up to the landing. After discussing the ways in which they might fit both the pickup and its trailer on the raft, they finally decided to make two trips.

As she started the outboard motor, Gabe couldn't suppress a momentary smugness when neither of the men jumped forward to do the job for her. Their acceptance of her abilities was one reason why she'd chosen them for what was almost certain to be a long summer spent in close contact.

She'd worked alongside wiry, gray-haired Elmer Gaines out on the Colville Reservation. Together they'd endured the discomfort of cold winds that whistled across the plateau of north-central Washington, and the hundred degree heat that could follow only a few days later. She knew she would hear no complaints from the old carpenter who'd once worked for her father no matter how difficult the job before them.

She didn't know the younger Turk Patterson as well, but so far he had cheerfully tackled any assignment she'd given him, accepting with equanimity the fact that his boss was a woman—a woman only two years older than he was, at that.

Gabe knew she would be able to tell whether she'd selected her crew wisely before long. At least she was confident of one important factor: She wouldn't be in a constant contest of wills over who was boss.

Close on the heels of that thought came the realization that that trust applied only to her crew. She didn't expect Phel Cannon to accord her the same respect, especially in light of what had taken place between them.

Elmer turned to study his young boss's face as it became suffused with furious color. She ran a finger inside her collar, separating the heavy flannel from her perspiring neck.

"Sun's getting hot already," she said lamely. She'd have to watch her wayward mind. She'd rather die than let either Turk or Elmer know how close she'd come to giving herself in flaming abandon to the owner of Wild Stag Island.

Turk's excited shout provided a welcome distraction from Gabe's burdensome thoughts. "Look!" He pointed excitedly at the shoreline, his round, boyish face alive with discovery. "It's an elk! There, see. He's knee-deep in the water."

They watched the regal beast in awe as he raised

his magnificent rack, looked haughtily at the intruders and bugled an echoing territorial challenge. After watching the raft approach until it was only a stone's throw away, the stately bull waded further into the water until he was shoulder deep and began to swim for the opposite shore.

"Wow!" Turk was obviously impressed. "This is going to be a fantastic summer, living right here where we can almost reach out and touch wild animals."

"Yes," Gabe agreed drily, knowing she'd already encountered the wildest animal of all—the man who could incite in her a savage, primitive passion such as she'd never before experienced. If she didn't keep a close rein on herself, resisting the responses Phel Cannon had stirred in her, how would she be able to walk away at the end of the summer?

As Gabe maneuvered the raft up to the dock so they could unload the trailer, she noted with hollow satisfaction that the cabin cruiser was gone from its mooring. No doubt Phel Cannon had taken her advice to consult an attorney. A lot of good it would do him, she thought. On one previous occasion she had met with just such reluctance to make use of her services, resulting in litigation. Since that time she had made certain that any contract she signed was ironclad. She was confident that any ethical attorney would advise Phel to gracefully acknowledge his contractual obligations and allow the work on the house to begin.

Gabe didn't intend to wait for a go-ahead. It took several hours to unload the trailer and ferry the pickup across the water. By noon the camper had been set up on blocks under a huge Ponderosa pine.

Whistling a tuneless melody, Turk made himself useful in the compact kitchen of the trailer, spreading mayonnaise and mustard on slices of rye bread while Gabe opened a can of frozen lemonade concentrate.

While Gabe and Turk prepared lunch, Elmer carried on a running commentary, peeling vegetables for a crockpot stew that would be their supper, about the quality of the food at various jobs he'd worked on. He'd learned long ago, as had Gabe, how much time could be lost from work if the crew knocked off to go into town to a restaurant every time someone was hungry. That was especially true in this instance, since a thirty-five-mile round-trip would be involved.

"I remember one time me and your daddy agreed to split the cooking chores," he reminisced. "He'd fix lunch every day and I'd do supper. Never got so tired of tuna fish in my life."

Gabe laughed as she took down plastic tumblers, squeezed past the burly Turk and put them on the table. Earlier she had considered the possibility of camping out with the crew, but that was before the camper arrived. The trailer was even smaller than she'd remembered. It would be inconsiderate of her to expect the guys to give up their own privacy. Besides, she reminded herself, rooming with the crew would establish a decidedly unbusinesslike precedent.

She'd just have to let Phel Cannon know in no uncertain terms that she intended to hold him to every clause of their agreement, including the provision of lodging. If the arrangement got too uncomfortable for him, he could just go elsewhere for the duration of her stay.

After the trio finished lunch Turk suggested they take a look around the island. Disappointment was apparent in his face when Gabe told him that she didn't want to lose any time before starting work on the foundation.

Gabe quickly stacked their dishes in the sink to be washed along with those from the evening meal. While Elmer and Turk unloaded the tools they would need, Gabe set up a folding drafting table, laid out the plans for the all-weather wood foundation and covered the blueprints with a large sheet of plexiglass to protect them, while still allowing her to refer to them easily.

Since the excavation and surveying were completed they set right to work, with Turk and Elmer carrying the heavy lumber to the sawhorses they had set up while Gabe measured and marked the boards to be cut. Before long the whine of an electric saw cut through the silence of the island.

Gabe yawned and stretched, complimented Elmer on his stew and said goodnight. She hurried up the hill toward the A-frame, shivering slightly in the chilly wind that blew across the lake. Twilight was fast slipping away and the quiet was broken only by the crickets and frogs singing in throaty unison as night fell on the island.

All afternoon Gabe had listened in vain for the roar of an approaching motor launch, anticipating and yet dreading Phel Cannon's return. While she wasn't eager to be reminded of their last angry confrontation, she would feel better knowing that his attorney had confirmed her position.

The empty cabin was still comfortably warm from the day's sun, and strangely welcoming. She filled the teakettle, fiddled with the propane stove until she figured out how to turn it on and set the kettle on the flame. In a few minutes she had a pot of aromatic tea steeping.

Wearily she carried the rest of the hot water to the tiny bathroom, taking care not to brush the blackened kettle against any of the clothing that hung along one side of the short, narrow corridor. She filled the little washbasin half full of cold water and warmed it with water from the kettle.

The sponge bath served to restore a feeling of cleanliness, but did nothing to ease the aching muscles that longed for a relaxing soak in a tub of luxuriant bubbles. It had been several weeks since she'd actually worked with any of the construction crews in her employ, so her muscles were strenuously protesting their hard day's work.

The unrelenting silence of the cabin was beginning to get on Gabe's nerves as she lit the kerosene lantern. What had begun as a comfortable feeling of solitude had developed into an uneasy feeling of isolation. She wished for a radio, for the sound of a human voice to relieve the stillness. And again she wondered, as she had when she reached the island, what had prompted its owner to build his home in such a solitary setting.

She considered building a fire to brighten the single room of the cabin, but decided it wasn't worth the bother. It seemed more sensible just to go to bed.

The trundle bed moved easily on its casters. Gabe was surprised by a shaky feeling in her midriff as she thought of Phel's visit to her bed during the previous night. Her throat constricted sharply as she considered what surely would have happened had he not uttered the words that had brought her out of the spiral of passion just before she slipped beyond retreat.

In the bathroom she changed into her pajamas, muttering a mild oath as she knocked her elbow against the wall and then the washbasin. She wondered how anyone Phel's size could maneuver in such a tiny room.

Gingerly rubbing the bruised joint, Gabe snuffed out the lantern and slipped into bed. The darkness seemed more intense than any she'd ever experienced and she felt more alone than she cared to admit.

Gabe had done a lot of thinking as she'd worked alongside Elmer and Turk all afternoon. She hadn't exactly arrived at a point where she could rationalize her response to Phel Cannon's lovemaking. But even to herself she confessed that she didn't feel disloyal to Buddie's memory. And she had come to the conclusion that it hadn't been a yearning for her lost husband—as she'd first thought—that had prompted her to respond so wantonly to Phel's midnight caresses.

The need that woke her in the night, bringing tears of loneliness, was simply a natural hunger for the physical satisfactions her marriage had introduced her to.

What she found so difficult to accept was the fact that she'd been so helplessly unable to resist the attraction that had produced sparks at the very first instant when she met Phel. He wasn't the gentle, thoughtful sort of man who usually appealed to her, a fact that made her response difficult to understand.

Gabrielle turned on her side and punched her pillow into a more comfortable position, sighing deeply. She really had gotten herself into a touchy situation. Grimly she remembered Phel's smoldering anger that morning. It wouldn't have been so bad if she hadn't overreacted to the situation and rebuffed him so viciously.

She was certain that the sexual tension between them, coupled with her belittling words, would drive an insurmountable wedge between them. It would be impossible for them to assume anything but the painfully polite attitude of strangers who were trapped in a stalled elevator and had to endure each other's company until rescue came.

And rescue would come only with the completion of the project that had brought her here. She couldn't afford—either financially, or in what it would cost her in self-respect—to abandon the contract.

Somehow, she knew instinctively, she must walk a carefully balanced course until she'd safely traversed the tightrope stretching across the next three months. Perhaps she could still salvage the remnants of her pride and finish the job with her professional dignity intact.

Somehow she must suppress any memory of Phel's lovemaking, forget how she had ignited like a Roman candle as he'd trailed kisses over her body. As she snuggled down deeper into the mattress she tried to push away the persistent memory of the previous night.

The sound of the cabin door opening brought Gabrielle out of her reverie into a state of instant alertness, her body suddenly tense. In the darkness she heard the match strike before its flare ignited the lantern's wick, casting a dim but inviting glow about the room.

Sitting up, Gabe pulled the heavy quilt up to her neck and faced Phel.

"I want to talk to you," he said.

"So, talk," she replied, still huddling behind the quilt as if it were a castle's battlements.

He eased his large frame into an easy chair. "I tend to think you'd rather come over here and talk to me rather than have me go over there to sit by you."

Gabrielle scrambled out of the trundle bed before he could finish the words, dragging the quilt along with her. She wasn't about to allow him to join her, considering what had happened the last time he'd done so.

Seated in the overstuffed chair opposite Phel, she tucked the quilt about her for warmth and the slight feeling of security it gave her. She looked at him expectantly.

"I want to start all over again with you," he began. "I know I hardly gave you a civil reception when you arrived yesterday."

"Hardly," she agreed.

"I'm sorry I was so . . ."

". . . chauvinistic?"

"Disagreeable," he amended.

"Something tells me your attorney told you your contract was binding."

"I consider all my contracts binding," he grated. "And what makes you think I consulted an attorney?"

"Didn't you?" Gabe raised an eyebrow in surprise.

"There was no reason to. I'm as eager as you are to get the house built."

"That wasn't your opinion yesterday."

"I've already apologized for that," Phel reminded her. "I have a profound dislike of deception and until I had time to think it over I felt that you'd deliberately deceived me."

"All right." Gabe expelled the breath she hadn't realized she was holding. "I gladly accept your apology and I'm relieved to know I can go ahead with the building without expending any negative energy on silly disputes."

She rose and extended her hand to confirm their new understanding. So quickly that she had no chance to resist, he grasped her hand and pulled her onto his lap. His arms locked her in a circle so firm that she stopped struggling almost immediately, knowing she was no match for his strength.

For a moment they sat motionless. Gabe was frozen in an uneasy awareness of their mutual attraction, a magnetism that seemed to switch on at the slightest touch.

Without making any demand on her other than that she remain there on his lap, Phel held her gently as he talked to her. At first he asked questions about the changes she'd made in the house plans, encouraging her to talk about her own experiences which had led her to make such design changes. After a few minutes Gabe warmed to the discussion, realizing that he was genuinely interested in what she had to say. She soon found herself relaxing in spite of the intimacy of their situation.

She thought several times that she should insist he release her, but by this time she had settled so comfortably into his cradling arms that she felt quite at home there.

"This seems a strange way to hold a conference between contractor and homeowner." She grinned engagingly. "It hardly seems businesslike."

"Maybe we should view it as a discussion between roommates," he teased. His arms tightened about her again as Gabe struggled to free herself once more. He stroked her shoulder and arm, gentling her until her resistance subsided before he spoke again. "You're as skittish as a fawn."

"It's a protective instinct." She was instantly sorry that she'd let him see just how vulnerable she was to him.

Phel smiled down at her and continued to rub her arm, moving his hand up to stroke the line of her shoulder, then further, to rub her temple soothingly. Much as she silently told herself that she should steel herself against the pleasure of his touch, Gabrielle found that she was rendered motionless by the comforting warmth of his fingers.

When she had sufficiently relaxed to feel the tension draining from her body, Phel loosened his hold, but still didn't let her go. "I want to get to know you." His lips were so close to her throat that Gabe could feel the vibration of the words. In spite of the warmth of his breath she felt a tiny chill that seemed to race along a throbbing nerve in her neck.

"I guess that will come naturally enough now that we're living together," he went on.

A protest rose to Gabe's lips before she glanced up to see the amusement in Phel's eyes. "Just because we'll be sharing the same quarters doesn't mean we'll be living together!"

"You'll like it here in the summertime," he said, ignoring her protest. His mouth had started to move from her temple to her ear, which he nuzzled with teasing deliberation. Gabrielle stiffened warily but didn't try to pull away, knowing how ineffective her earlier struggle had been.

Strong lean fingers stroked the back of her head, following the elegant shape of her nape to her shoulder and then returning to touch her hair lightly.

"I like your hair," he murmured into it. "It's soft as doeskin." His voice had become husky.

"Sometimes in winter when the lake is frozen the deer come across the ice. They're afraid of me at first, but the winters are long and harsh. Long before spring they're eating out of my hand."

Just like *she* was doing!

Gabe swallowed convulsively, pushing with all her might to try to put a little distance between them. Without exerting any pressure he held her still, his arms appearing to be relaxed, although his grip was too firm to allow her to slide away.

"Phel!" Her voice sounded breathless even to her own ears. "I've had a long hard day and I have to get up early again tomorrow."

"I know," he whispered against her ear. In a single motion he rose and set her on her feet, dropping a light kiss on her brow.

A shiver of excitement and yearning coursed through her and it was all Gabe could do to force herself to leave his arms. How warm and precious those few minutes had been. She felt deprived as she turned away, even though that was what she'd thought she wanted as Phel had held her.

What strange contradictory reactions this man stirred in her! Of course it was foolish of her to take him seriously when he'd probably only been amusing himself with her.

When the morning came, bringing the cold light of day, he'd probably revert to his overbearing ways again, which would leave her feeling even more foolish if she responded to his overtures tonight.

She'd never before met anyone whose masculinity so overwhelmed her. Every time they came near each other sparks flew. She didn't know exactly how to handle her response to his sensual invitation.

Gabe's hazel eyes reflected her troubled mind when she looked up at Phel for long, unguarded moments. Just for an instant the intensity of his blue gaze increased and she thought he would sweep her into his arms again.

"You'd better get some rest," he said at last.

Gabrielle turned away, pulling up the trailing

quilt about her before he added, "Instead of a cold shower, I think I'll take a long walk in the cool night air."

It seemed but the blink of an eye until it was daylight again.

Just as quickly as she had sensed it was morning, Gabe became aware of the rich aroma of coffee perking, mixed with a subtle fragrance of after-shave lingering in the cabin. She sat up and looked around to find she was alone in the room. But the rumpled bed a few feet away was mute testimony to its occupancy during the night.

Gabe found it disconcerting to realize that she hadn't heard Phel come in when he'd returned to the cabin. He'd slept there, in the next bed, without her knowledge.

Rising, she picked up her coveralls and tee shirt and scurried into the bathroom to dress. The coffeepot was sputtering as it boiled over on the flame when she returned to the main room. She hurried to the stove, wrapped a dishtowel about her arm so she wouldn't be burned by the boiling coffee as she turned down the flame and eased the pot over to the side of the burner. After pouring a cup of the scalding brew, she carried it out onto the porch and perched on the railing, where she sipped the eye-opening liquid.

Across the little meadow she could see Phel and Elmer, engaged in easy conversation as they inspected the progress from the day before. Gabe wished she were close enough to hear what Phel had to say about their work.

That wish was to be denied, she saw as she started down the hill to join the two men. Before she had taken half a dozen steps Phel Cannon turned away and ambled out onto the dock. Gabe was fairly certain that he hadn't looked her way, so it didn't appear that he was leaving just because she had decided to join them.

Only a moment later the roar of the cabin cruiser confirmed that Phel was leaving the island. With only a momentary sense of disappointment, she assured herself that the day would go much smoother if she didn't have to spend any time worrying about him.

Elmer looked up as Gabe advanced and extended a hand to her as she mounted the uneven pile of dirt and rock from the excavation. He turned and waved at the retreating boat, then leveled smoky-colored eyes at his boss. "Nice fella, that Cannon."

With a twinge of something closely related to regret, Gabrielle thought that his assessment was probably more accurate than her own initial reaction had been. Phel Cannon probably *was* a nice fellow. But fate had thrown them into adversarial roles. In spite of his assurance that he wanted to make a new beginning with her, Gabe found it hard to forget how strongly he'd resisted the idea that she was going to build his house. And nothing could take away the hateful words she'd flung at him when she'd awakened in his arms. Thanks to circumstances, she'd probably still be wondering what he really thought of her when the summer was over and the job finished.

She was stung into replying, "Maybe you see a

different side of him than he presents to me. Anyway, I haven't got time to try to figure him out."

Elmer pursed his lips and looked inquiringly at Gabe, his surprise at her uncharacteristic rancor barely concealed. "Funny you should say that, Missy Gabe. He seemed perfectly straightforward to me."

Gabe shrugged and looked away. "What's keeping Turk? I said I wanted to start at half-past six."

"He's wandering around, looking at the flora and fauna, I reckon," Elmer guessed. "Maybe if we start sawing some logs he'll get the message."

Gabe resisted the temptation to ask Elmer what Phel had had to say about the work they'd begun the previous day. At least with him gone she'd be able to get some work done, she fretted silently.

After pulling on leather work gloves, she extracted a steel tape measure from her carpenter's apron. "Let's get going then," she said, putting aside her concern about what Phel Cannon might be up to.

By midmorning Gabe had fallen into the rhythm of her work and was thankful that her body had quickly adapted to what was actually her normal pace. The sun had climbed high in the cloudless sky and the day was so warm that she didn't need any encouragement to take a break when Turk went to the camper to fetch iced tea.

Gabe wondered how long it would be until the utility company would finish laying the underwater cable that would bring electricity to the island. She hadn't talked to Phel long enough to ascertain the completion schedule. She did know from their pre-contract correspondence that he maintained a generator to supply his own frugal needs. The portable generator on the truck was sufficient to operate the power tools and provide the camper with enough juice to run the small refrigerator and lights.

They could enjoy a few small luxuries, such as the ice cubes in her glass, but Elmer and Turk would have to rely on the evening breezes off the lake to cool the little trailer; it reached intolerable temperatures during the day despite the shade from the pine trees.

With a sigh Gabe acknowledged to herself that if comfort were all that was important to her she would have chosen a different line of work. Anyway, most of her life had been spent in little more than adequate living quarters, so this was nothing new.

In reality, it wasn't the lack of amenities that was grating on her nerves, but the necessity of sharing the primitive accommodations with a man who could—by his immense size and presence—make any room seem tiny. How many more nocturnal interludes could she endure when it took only the brush of his hand to turn her blood to flame?

With a grunt Gabe got to her feet. She shrugged away the course her thoughts were taking, fearing that it would soon lead her to even more unsettling images. After all, she hadn't even heard Phel come in the night before. Why worry about it now when there was work to be done?

She gathered the glasses and carried them to the camper. When she returned Turk was grumbling goodnaturedly about a slave-driving boss. Gabe bristled a little until she caught Elmer's laughing eyes and realized that Turk was just having a joke at her expense.

Turk had removed his shirt and wore only a pair of cutoff jeans. Gabe idly watched him as he picked up a log and slid it onto the sawhorse, his muscled torso rippling in the sunshine. It struck her as amusing that the younger man seemed unaware that there were only the three of them on the island and, consequently, no one to impress as he strutted about, flexing his muscles like a cocky rooster.

The threesome had just returned to their labors when the quiet of the lake was broken by the hum of a motorboat in the distance. Gabe kept her eyes on the piece of lumber she was sawing. Several times the day before she'd heard an approaching boat and looked up, only to see a fishing party or water skiers passing by.

"Looks like the big *cahuna* is back," Turk observed.

Gabe threw a glance at the launch just as the engine was cut. Rippling waves slapped against the dock and the pebbly beach as the boat glided into the slip. Gabe straightened and stretched her aching neck and shoulder muscles, watching with an air of feigned disinterest as Phel Cannon stepped onto the dock and turned to offer a hand to his passenger.

The girl who accepted his help looked fragile and light, as if the wind might whisk her away if she didn't have a strong arm to cling to. She was wearing a deliciously feminine little dress of gauzy apricot-colored cotton and, even from this distance, looked as delectable as that blushing, softly

50

ripe fruit. Her hair was a shiny cap of glossy black, molding the graceful curve of her head.

Standing near Gabe, Turk and Elmer emitted long, low whistles in unison. Elmer doffed his scruffy hat as the newcomers reached them. Turk grinned his pleasure and reached to assist the girl over the rocky pile of dirt.

Phel made the introductions and the girl, who Phel introduced as Marlene Tennyson, solemnly shook each hand in turn. When she came to Gabe she had to look up a considerable distance to meet the hazel eyes that warily studied her. Gabe extended her hand, suddenly acutely aware of her own tousled hair and sunburned nose. She withdrew her hand quickly and stuck it in her coverall pocket as though she might be required to offer it again.

A hurt, puzzled look flickered in the girl's turquoise eyes before she smiled. "I'm really pleased to meet you," she said in a lilting voice. "I hope we get to know each other well while you are here."

There was nothing offensive in the words, but Gabe wondered if she detected a subliminal message that the speaker would still be here when *she* herself was gone. Almost instantly she decided that the thought was unworthy, the sort of reaction she had thought herself above.

"Marlene is sort of my housekeeper," Phel informed the group. He looked down at the tiny brunette protectively. "But she's really much more than that. I think she knows how much I appreciate her coming out from Polson once a week to take care of me."

Gabe groaned inwardly as Marlene looked at

Phel with an adoration so profound that it was almost tangible. An unwarranted pang of resentment shot through Gabe, causing her to look away in confusion.

"What are friends for?" Marlene asked. "We really are *very* old friends," she explained to the others.

Gabe wondered uncharitably how they could be such *very* old friends when the girl looked as if she were still a year or two shy of twenty.

"When I saw how much work you'd accomplished yesterday"—Phel's words claimed Gabe's attention, pulling her out of her own silent discourse —"it occurred to me what long hours the three of you will be putting in. I've asked Marlene to come out every day to take care of the cooking and tidy up for everyone."

Before Gabe could protest Elmer and Turk let out spontaneous yelps of glee. "Hot dog!" Elmer whooped. "This is going to be one fine job if I don't have to eat this here turkey's cooking." He pushed Turk playfully, grinning at Marlene like a love-smitten teenager. "In case you're wondering, Miz Tennyson, 'Turk' is short for Turkey."

"I'll remember that come next Thanksgiving." The girl laughed melodically. Then, becoming more serious, she asked, "Could I get one of you fellows to help me carry all those grocery bags up from the boat so you can all have some lunch?"

Gabe bit back an acrimonious reply, knowing she would just look spiteful. If they wanted to fall all over themselves to do Marlene's bidding it would draw no comment from her.

"I'll help you, Marly." Phel settled the matter.

"You're supposed to be here to make the work go faster, not to borrow Mrs. Seberg's crew to do domestic chores."

As Phel and Marlene headed toward the boat, Gabe pulled on her gloves. "All right," she said irritably. "You heard what the man said. You're supposed to be building a house, not standing around gawking at the scenery."

3

~oooooooooo~

Lunch was a lighthearted, bantering affair, an impromptu picnic served on the porch of the A-frame. Phel had brought out a wobbly, decrepit picnic table, a legacy from the cabin's previous owner, and hosed it off.

His booming laugh ringing out across the meadow, Turk had insisted that the rickety benches would never hold the boss lady's weight. He'd made a big production of administering first aid in the form of a few quickly driven nails.

It should have been fun, but for Gabe the knotted pain in her midsection curbed her appetite for the golden-brown fried chicken and potato salad Marlene dished up alongside baked beans and light, puffy yeast rolls dripping with butter.

All she could think about was the possibility that Turk or Elmer might for some reason enter the cabin and discover the intimacy of her accommodations. They knew the contract provided for her lodging and she hadn't disabused them of their natural assumption that she had a room of her own.

Had Phel mentioned the arrangements to anyone? Marlene? Did the girl laughing across the table know Gabe had spent the last two nights alone with Phel in the dark intimacy of the tiny cabin?

There was nothing in Marlene's manner to indicate that she was privy to the information. The girl was just as warmly generous and friendly toward Gabe as she was to any of the men. In fact, she was such a sweet, unassuming young woman that Gabe was unable to find any fault with her, other than her transparent worship of Phel Cannon. That gave Gabe some cause to wonder if Marlene was as innocent as she appeared, and just as quickly she wondered if she should take the younger girl aside and offer some sisterly advice about the danger of being taken in by an experienced man.

As she finished an icy glass of lemonade, Gabe felt her face flame in premature embarrassment when Turk offered to help Marlene clear the table. One glance into the cabin was all it would take for him to get a pretty clear picture of the sleeping arrangements. It seemed to Gabe that her position as boss would be threatened if anything lessened Turk's respect for her.

Gabe looked up to see Phel studying her, his lips slightly pursed, a curious expression on his face. Before either of them could speak, Marlene shooed Turk and Elmer away from the table.

"You just don't ask me to lift any of those logs and I won't expect you to wash any dishes," she laughed. "I think everyone should do what they're best qualified to do."

"Well, Turk," Elmer hooted. "That gets you off the hook. You won't have to do *anything!*"

"Let's get back to work now," Gabe broke into their teasing exchange. "If we really hit it now we can knock off a little earlier than we did yesterday."

"Polson's semi-infallible weather forecaster says we'll have a high in the nineties today," Phel said. "Since our bathing facilities are so primitive, you might all enjoy a late afternoon swim to cool off."

Gabe's distaste for the idea was written on her face. All she needed was another muddy encounter in the lake. "That sounds like a good way to get dirtier."

Phel seemed to relish her discomfort. She knew he could probably follow the course of her thoughts, which were taking her back to their struggle in the water. Her mind flew back to those moments when their anger had so suddenly dissolved into passion. She could almost feel the strength of his thighs pressing so strongly against her own flailing limbs.

"The water's only dirty if you stir up the mud on the bottom." Phel's sapphire eyes danced with silent humor. "But we can take the raft out into the lake where the water is crystal clear, if you'd enjoy that more."

Gabrielle could see only futility in objecting further. Perhaps the prospect of a refreshing swim was just what she and the guys needed to get them through a hot afternoon in the sun. She began to look forward to the idea—even though Phel Cannon would undoubtedly be there.

By late afternoon Gabe's head was ringing from the constant whine of the electric saw and the heat of the sun. She wore a visor on an elasticized bandeau to shade her eyes and give her nose a little protection from the burning rays, but the crown of her head was unprotected from the unaccustomed heat.

She thought about going into the cabin to look for some aspirin, but she didn't want to appear to be coddling herself, so she worked on as the temperature continued to rise.

At about four o'clock Elmer pulled out a large red handkerchief and mopped his ruddy face. "I can't hack this any longer. It's hotter'n Hades," he grumbled. "You 'bout ready for a dip, Missy Gabe?"

"I sure am," she responded without hesitation. "I'll go change into my suit and be down at the dock in five minutes."

At the entrance to the cabin Gabe knocked hesitantly, then pushed the door open. To her dismay, the swinging door bumped against Phel and Marlene, causing all three of them to jump in surprise.

"Sorry," Gabe mumbled in embarrassment, assuming she had interrupted an embrace. "The guys are ready for their promised reward, so I need to change."

"Are you going to join us, Marly?" Phel asked the question smoothly, unperturbed by the awkward silence that had claimed the two women.

"Not this time." Marlene smiled brightly. "I don't have a suit here. If it's all right, Phel, I'll just take the launch to town and bring it back in the morning. That way you can enjoy a swim and not have to bother about taking me home."

Phel assured her that it was no bother to take her into Polson, but made no effort to dissuade her. "Just be careful with the Eagle. I'm much too fond of you to have anything happen to you."

"He's just being funny." Marlene winked saucily at Gabe. "He knows I can pilot that boat as well as he can."

Gabe stood uncomfortably watching, not knowing what to make of the teasing exchange. When Phel dropped an arm around the younger girl's shoulder and squeezed affectionately, Gabe stifled a cutting retort and turned away, unable to endure witnessing the look of adoration on Marlene's face.

"If you'll excuse me, I'll go change," she muttered, and scooped up her duffelbag from the corner so she could escape to the bathroom.

Alone, Gabe sizzled in silence, cursing Phel for deliberately taunting her, and herself for responding like a gauche newcomer to the male/female sparring that typified the mating dance. Stilling the cry of denial that sprang to her lips at the thought, Gabe stripped off her coveralls. This was nothing like that, she thought angrily. But, then, what was it?

Why should she worry about what prompted her response to Phel Cannon's every look and action? The thing she needed to concentrate on wasn't an analysis of her feelings, but a suppression of them!

Gabrielle rummaged through the contents of her

bag and thought of wearing cutoffs instead of her much-too-revealing maillot, but discarded the idea as thoughts of Phel's ogling appreciation of her soggy tee shirt on the occasion of her last dip in Flathead's waters tormented her.

With a little shiver of remembrance she slipped into the deceptively simple one-piece suit of shimmering pale green nylon and grabbed a towel from the rod to cover it.

When she reached the dock Phel looked up from where he was untying a mooring line.

Gabe thought inconsequentially that he must have acquired his swim trunks before he left California. The skimpy black briefs laced up the sides, revealing smoothly tanned skin. The suit was decidedly sophisticated alongside Turk's cutoffs and the bright yellow polka-dotted Bermudas that came almost to Elmer's bony knees.

She apologized for keeping them waiting as she walked onto the raft and sank down on a pile of towels, watching silently. Phel poled the raft away from the dock to a point several hundred yards out from both the island and the shore of the mainland.

Before he could drop the anchor to hold the raft in position, Turk executed a fairly commendable dive. With little urging Elmer followed feet first and surfaced a few yards away.

"Come on in, boss lady," he called through chattering teeth. "T'ain't *very* cold."

Steeling herself for the shock of icy water, Gabe stepped off into the lake. Underwater, she opened her eyes to find that Phel had been right. The water was sparkling, deep green in its depths, lightening almost to the clarity of drinking water near the surface.

She began an easy breaststroke and was only inches from breaking water when a hand clasped her ankle. Remembering what had happened when she'd fought Phel before, she was determined to avoid the same mistake. Allowing her body to relax and drift until it bobbed to the surface like a log, Gabe spun about suddenly and reached into the water to entwine her fingers in her aquatic opponent's hair.

She shook the water out of her eyes and gasped in surprise as she looked directly into Turk's laughing eyes.

"You! Don't you ever do that to me again unless you want to check into the union hall to look for a job!" Her sudden anger was so intense that it charged the air between them.

"Aww. Come on, Gabe." Turk's laughter was swallowed in a gulp of confusion over what might have spawned such wrath from his usually good-natured boss. "You don't have to pull rank on me. I was only kidding around."

Gabe pushed herself away and stroked toward the raft. The hand that reached to assist her out of the water was warm and steadying. She couldn't say the same about the pair of deep blue eyes that regarded her in unabashed speculation as Phel draped a thick velour beach towel about her shivering shoulders.

"Don't you think you were a little bit harsh with him?"

"Don't you think it's about time some men

learned not to grab every female form that gets within grabbing distance?"

Gabe snatched off the towel and spread it out so she could lie down on it, hoping the sun would warm her. Phel spread another towel and stretched his long length disturbingly close to her. He propped himself up on an elbow and studied the woman beside him.

"You sound so ferocious." His voice had become a velvety caress that sent a fresh shiver along Gabe's spine. With tantalizing slowness, Phel traced the same invisible line from the wet hair at her nape until his fingertip brushed the dimpled curve just below her waist where her swimsuit dipped to reveal the swell of her hips.

"I'd be more convinced that you're a spitting cat if I hadn't already heard the kitten purr."

Turning her face away so he couldn't see how upsetting she found his remark, not to mention his touch, Gabe snapped, "I thought you were dying for a swim!"

"That's not very perceptive of you, my sweet Gabrielle. The only thing I'm dying to do is make love to you."

She was on the verge of diving for the safety of the lake when she heard his splash. She put her arm across her face to shield her eyes and tried to still her thudding heart.

Although Gabe had never expressed her feelings out loud, Phel seemed to sense her reluctance to admit either Turk or Elmer to the cabin. When the swim party returned to the dock Phel suggested that they all dine in the camper since it afforded the luxury of electricity.

"Marlene has prepared something that can be easily heated," he assured them. "As soon as Gabe gets dressed she can help me carry the food down."

When they reached the trailer a short while later they found the small table already set for four. Gabe placed a large bowl of shrimp salad on the table while Turk popped a fragrant, cheesy casserole into the microwave oven. Elmer rambled on, asking questions about the lake and local fishing as he poured coffee.

Announcing that she would sit in back so she wouldn't have to wait on anyone, Gabrielle slid to the inside of the upholstered bench that turned into a bed when the table was lowered to meet it. It seemed to her that Phel sat a little closer to her than necessary, but upon reflection she decided that she was acting a bit paranoid. The booth was too narrow to allow either one of them any more elbow room.

Conversation during the meal turned inevitably to shop talk, with each of the carpenters taking a turn at relating some of his less dignified experiences in the trade. Gabe found herself enjoying the exchange, although her mind strayed all too often to the warmth of the muscular thigh pressed so intimately against her own.

When the conversation moved on to hunting and fishing Gabrielle excused herself, slipping out quickly when Phel rose to let her pass. Unobtrusively she began to clear the table. By the time she had finished the few dishes and stored them away in the cupboard above the little sink, the men were deeply engrossed in Phel's narrative about a raft trip down the Clark Fork River.

Quietly she slipped out and hurried through the night to the A-frame. In less than ten minutes she had finished her nightly routine and was snuggled deep in her quilt, grateful for the few minutes of solitude so she could go over the day's events in her mind.

But before she could take in the implications of Phel's apparent change in attitude toward her, or ponder the relationship Marlene might enjoy with him, weariness took over and soothed the complexity of emotions roiling within her to leave only the restful oblivion of sleep.

4

〰〰〰〰〰〰〰〰

Gabe made her way through a grove of white-barked aspen, picking her way over giant rocks and fallen moss-covered logs. By the time she reached the rocky outcropping that was the highest point on Wild Stag Island she was grateful for the chance to stop and catch her breath.

Two weeks had passed since she'd come to the island and this was the first time she'd given herself a break to explore it. She'd been surprised as she'd climbed to see how large the island was.

At twilight the air was still where she stood, but she could hear the wind above her in the towering pines, murmuring as constantly as the ocean surf.

Seating herself on a flat rocky ledge, she found she could see in all directions. It was, as she had guessed, a perfect spot to watch the sunset. Below her, at the edge of the meadow, she could just make out the pile of logs and neatly stacked lumber near the shore. In her imagination she could picture herself standing on the deck of the beautiful log home that would soon begin to rise on the newly completed foundation.

The panorama to be seen from the deck which would thrust out over the water was nothing short of awe inspiring. The waters of Flathead, the largest fresh-water lake west of the Mississippi River, stretched in all directions. Gabe wondered just how much of the lake's almost two hundred square miles could be seen from her present vantage point.

Across the narrow inlet, on the mainland, she could see a few lights blinking on as the twilight deepened. Probably from a few summer homes, she thought, remembering that Phel had said very few of the houses were occupied all year round.

To the east lay a larger area of the lake, its shore darkened by deep forests of pine and fir. Gabe could see several smaller islands dotting the water near the shore. Beyond that, rising into the amethyst sky, the Mission Mountains looked purple in the dusk. Gabe shivered a little as she wondered how late into the summer the mountains would wear their crowns of snow.

Her attention was caught by a swooping shadow. She strained her eyes to follow the soaring flight of the giant bird. It wasn't until the bald eagle settled on the craggy limb of a dead tree that she could identify it as the majestic white-headed emblem of America.

She sat silently watching the eagle for a few

minutes, envying the bird its freedom to fly away from any danger that threatened. How she wished that she too were free to fly where she chose.

In a short time she would have to return to the cabin, where she knew Phel would be waiting. All through the evening meal he'd remained at her side like a solicitous lover, until even Elmer had raised an eyebrow in an unspoken question that left Gabe turning aside to conceal her furious blush.

If she had the strong wings of an eagle she could make her escape from the sapphire eyes that seemed to be watching her every time she looked up from her work. She wouldn't be bound by legal contract or headstrong determination to stay in this untenable situation for the entire summer, mentally thrashing herself hour after hour for her own helpless inability to handle Phel's attentions with any degree of composure.

It had been so much easier when he'd shouted and waved his arms angrily, declaring that he'd never allow her to build his home. At least then she'd known where she stood with him: She had been his enemy.

But, then, that hadn't changed. He was still her foe. She wasn't sure if it were his constant pursuit or her own wild response to it that caused such a steady erosion of her self-assurance. There was nothing uplifting to the spirit about being the object of a campaign of seduction, she thought. At least not when there was no love involved, only a strange mix of chemistry.

She wouldn't allow the fact that Phel seemed to win every skirmish to stampede her into conceding the war. She had to armor herself against the rush of sensation she experienced each time he accidentally brushed against her. She would learn, somehow, to still the cascade of yearning that charged through her veins at the mere sight of his muscular frame in the distance.

Gabe raised her eyes to the thin silvery crescent that hovered just above the distant skyline and watched as the last pale lemony band of light faded into darkness. All around her the chirping of the night insects echoed a soothing message. Don't panic. Don't panic.

She could no longer see the eagle on his craggy perch. Perhaps he had flown away, unseen, into the fading light. If only, she thought again, she were free to do the same.

Fast on the heels of the wistful thought came the knowledge that if she were really free of the constraints she had placed upon herself she could just abandon herself to Phel's siege of her senses and become the willing victim of his assault.

If she were only free to do as her heart desired, she would simply throw herself into his arms and plead with him to make love to her until all the wild, hungry longing within her was assuaged.

Phel looked up from a magazine as Gabe entered the cabin. "I was beginning to wonder if I should send the posse out to look for you."

"I was watching the sunset," was Gabe's hesitant reply. She was glad when he didn't remind her that the sun had set a full hour earlier.

Gabe excused herself and went into the tiny bathroom to perform her bedtime ritual. She returned to sit down next to the blazing fire, wondering how she would ever be able to lie down and go to sleep with both her mind and her nerves coiled as tight as a bedspring.

"You look troubled," Phel said with real concern in his voice. "Is there anything I can do to fix whatever's wrong?"

"Not unless you can conjure up a long, hot bath for me," Gabe replied without thinking. "I'm not Spartan enough to endure the cold shower with the garden hose, like you do." She rubbed the back of her neck as she spoke. "Sponge baths may keep me clean enough, but they don't relax the muscles like a good bath."

Without hesitation Phel stood up. "All you have to do is ask and it's yours."

Before Gabe could reply he had vanished. She could hear him rummaging around in the storage area behind the A-frame, followed by a noisy metallic clank as he accidentally banged something against the porch steps. The tattoo of water spraying on metal, like hail on a tin roof, only increased her curiosity.

"Oh, no!" she cried as Phel wrestled a long, oval-shaped, galvanized tub through the door. The metal tank was the sort used to water livestock and was about five feet long.

"Well, it's not the ritziest, but if you *really do* want a bath, it seems to me . . ."

"Oh, I didn't mean to sound like a snob; it's just that . . ." Gabe stammered. "I mean, how will I get it into the bathroom? It's too long!"

Phel's mouth twitched with suppressed humor as he studied the tub. "The few times I've used it I just put it in front of the fireplace so it's nice and cozy."

"But . . ."

"I understand your desire for privacy." Phel crossed his arms over his chest and lounged against the door. "But I think you can see that the only way you could get a tub of this size into the bathroom would be to stand it on end."

"You think that's amusing, don't you?"

"I think I'll fill a big kettle with water and put it on the stove to heat," Phel said softly, seemingly unperturbed by her rising ire. "By the time the water's hot you should be ready to hop in."

"And what do you think *you're* going to do while I'm taking my bath?" she asked hotly.

"Since the tub's not big enough for both of us, I guess I'll have to wait my turn."

"Surely you don't think I'm just going to take a bath while you're right here . . . right here where . . ."

"Gabrielle, if you don't go ahead and get ready I'm going to fill the tub and just throw you in it." Phel's voice was so soft that he might have been humoring a fretful child, but it had an underlying hardness that assured her he wouldn't hesitate to make good his threat.

"All right!" she fumed. "Get the water ready."

When she emerged from the bathroom some ten minutes later, carrying a rose-scented bath oil and a bottle of shampoo, Phel was refilling a large kettle after having emptied its contents into the tub. Gabe's face wore a look of triumph when he turned to face her, then did a double take as he observed her attire.

The flesh-colored camisole and lacy briefs of a soft silky fabric were provocatively demure, promising much more than was revealed by the artful cut of the expensive lingerie. Gabe smiled smugly as she approached the tub and tested the water.

"It's not quite warm enough to be comfortable," she said as she poured the fragrant oil into the tub.

"I'll have another kettle hot in a minute."

Gabe didn't speak as Phel studied her feminine undergarments with great interest. She silently congratulated herself on her choice. In spite of the seductive nature of the sleek lingerie—which she'd bought because she sometimes felt she needed the psychological lift of ultra-feminine underwear to counter the rough appearance of her work clothing —she knew it was actually less revealing than many of her tank tops or halters.

Phel splashed the steaming water into the tub and turned to refill the kettle from the cold water tap at the sink. "Just in case you need a warmup later," he said gruffly as Gabrielle settled into the water with a grateful sigh.

"Oh, this is heavenly," she crooned, leaning back and closing her eyes. "I'm glad you talked me into it."

Phel retired to his easy chair and was soon absorbed in his magazine again. At least that was the appearance he was trying to create, Gabe decided as she looked up to find him watching her.

Determinedly, she went about the chore of soaping her long, slender legs. She didn't deign to reply when Phel offered to wash her back, just scooted down so she could submerge her short curly locks. Sitting up again, she rubbed the creamy shampoo into her wet hair and then ducked her head again to rinse away the suds.

Reaching blindly for the washcloth she had hung over the side of the tub, Gabe's groping hand touched a rolled-up shirt sleeve and brushed across the bristling hair on Phel's forearm. Her fingers shook uncontrollably as she grasped the textured cloth he handed her.

When she'd wiped the sudsy water away from her eyes she dipped the cloth into the rapidly cooling water and patted her suddenly flaming cheeks to cool them.

"You'll be courting pneumonia if you don't get out of that tub before the water gets any colder." Phel's voice was curiously gruff.

Knowing that it would do her no good to stall any longer, Gabe stood up, the water cascading from her shivering frame. A quick look down at the wet silk and stretch lace molding her breasts told her she'd made a serious tactical error. Not by any stretch of the imagination could nudity be as evocative as the imprint of each suddenly taut nipple outlined against the damp fabric.

He reached for her almost blindly, lifting her from the water as though she were weightless, and buried his face in her damp bosom.

"Oh, Gabrielle!" His voice was muffled as his lips evoked a stinging response from her icy skin, heating the tiny beads of moisture clinging to her rose-scented collarbone.

Gabe thought of the oft-heard admonition to avoid contact with an electrical current when standing in water and felt, with a heady exhilaration, the effect of the two erupting to fuse her pliant, unresisting body to his hard torso.

All the aching longing of the past weeks surged

through her and her senses spun in delirium as Phel's mouth claimed hers. Gabrielle's lips opened under his expert tutelage like blossoms warmed by the sun. Her tongue caressed his as he learned all the intimate crevices of her mouth. Wave after wave of aftershock jolted through her, weakening her knees still further. He had lifted her completely off the floor and of their own volition her long, shapely legs encircled his strong hips.

Gabe was scarcely aware of Phel's movements as he crossed the room silently, all the while unwilling to break the contact of their lips as though they shared a common air supply. It seemed as though her lungs would rupture in the rarefied atmosphere.

With one hand he spread the oversized bath sheet he'd offered her a moment before. Gently he lowered her before the crackling fire. Then his hands moved swiftly to pull her wet garment over her head. The glow of the fire against her skin was insignificant compared to the raging flames that heated her from within.

Almost reverently Phel's hands cupped her breasts before he lowered his head to claim a hardening nipple between his gently teasing teeth. Gabe gasped in delight as his hands moved over her taut stomach to find the moist core of her longing.

Frantically her fingers tore at the buttons of his shirt while her body's unconscious movements shamelessly echoed a rhythm as old as time. As his shirt fell away her fingers explored the musculature of his broad chest, glorying in the contrast of smooth skin and rough-textured hair.

Her senses were filled with the warm male scent of him, the sound of his husky voice murmuring her name, the feel of his hard masculine flesh.

Phel pressed his face to her throat and muffled a groan of excitement as her fingers fluttered over his turquoise-studded silver belt buckle, seeking to release it. That his desire matched her own was evident in every hard line of his body.

As Gabe raised her lips again, beseeching his to drown her in rapture, she cried out in surprise as a spark from the blazing fire burned her arm before she could pinpoint the source of the pain.

Phel and Gabe leapt to their feet in unison as the fire crackled with a series of pops as loud as firecrackers. Their quick movement saved them from possible injury as a heavy log rolled in a shower of sparks, its momentum carrying it through the makeshift screen to a resting place on the edge of the hearth.

Before Gabe could react Phel had picked up a poker, with which he quickly maneuvered the offending log back into the fireplace.

By the time he returned his attention to Gabrielle she stood wrapped in the bath sheet, the realization of how nearly she'd succumbed to desire evident in her shocked white face.

"Are you all right?" Phel's voice was filled with concern. "Were you burned?"

"Almost," Gabe returned wryly, deliberately alluding to the flames of passion rather than the fire's sparks. "I guess I came close, but I'm all right now."

"Gabe . . ."

Her chin came up in quivering defiance as she pushed aside the last faint lingering shadow of the magic that had enveloped them only moments before. She brushed aside the hands reaching for her and turned away.

"Gabrielle!" His voice held a note of frustration. "I just don't understand you. How can you just turn it off? Nothing can convince me you were only teasing. I know a tease when I see one, and you don't fit the description."

"No," she replied softly. "I wasn't teasing; I was . . . I was carried away." The pain in her soft tone was replaced by a harder note. "I know you won't understand, Phel, but I can't let that happen to me." She felt the panic rising in her throat at her inability to find the words to explain. "I want to have control over my life, not just let life *happen* to me. I don't *want* to be swept off my feet. To just give in to irrational urges."

When Phel looked as though he would sweep aside her protestations she became more defensive. "And I don't need or want a master to enslave me." Her shoulders slumped slightly as she looked up, imploring him to understand.

Her words only hinted at the depth of her feelings. In her heart she knew a truth she couldn't afford to let him know. So intense was her response to Phel's every touch that she had no doubt at all that to allow him to become her lover would create a bondage she couldn't endure without the tempering element of love.

"I have to make my own choices." She looked at him with only a small hope that he would understand her reasoning.

"Have you thought of choosing to let it happen?"

"That's a cop-out!" she cried. "If I used that sort of rationale, I wouldn't be making a conscious choice, I'd only be losing myself in the moment."

"Have you forgotten the wonder of that moment?"

Gabrielle wondered why he had to ask. Wasn't the response he'd just evoked from her testimony to the fact? What more proof did he need that her own responses were in sync with his own?

So magnetic was the attraction that pulled her into Phel Cannon's arms that she knew it would be difficult to resist him in any situation. If she relented —allowed herself to taste the rapture—wouldn't it make her subject to an addiction she couldn't afford to risk?

5

A slight breeze fluttered the sheaf of blueprinted pages as Gabrielle lifted the plexiglass sheet to turn the house plans to a new section. The subfloor and framing had been completed and the walls were going up.

As Gabe studied the details of the exterior walls she lowered her brow in a perplexed frown. Although her eyes remained on the printed page as she covered it with the clear paperweight once more, the construction project was the furthest thing from her mind.

It was a wonder she got any work done at all, she thought. It seemed to her that Phel Cannon occupied her mind to the exclusion of all else.

Why couldn't the diagram for life be as simple as the plan for a building? If there were a detailed blueprint to follow, so she wouldn't just have to ricochet from one encounter to the next, wouldn't the construction of a new relationship go much smoother? Or would there always be the conflict, the uncertainties?

Since the night the rolling log had interrupted their lovemaking, Phel had withdrawn a discreet distance—far enough away to give Gabe a little breathing space, and still close enough to lend a hand with a difficult chore or to provide her with a nurturing cup of tea when she returned to the cabin on a chilly evening.

He had made a concerted effort in the past week to see to her comfort during the long evenings in the cabin. He had listened sympathetically as she talked about the problems associated with construction on the rocky island site, never finding fault with her methods of dealing with them.

He had proven to be conversant in an endless variety of subjects, all of which seemed to Gabe to have been carefully selected, uncontroversial topics that promised only a spirited discussion with little room for serious disagreement.

She had almost gotten to the point where she could relax around him, could almost enjoy his solicitous company. But she couldn't quite shake the feeling that there was danger in her complacency. How long would he be content to entertain her through the evening, only to conveniently melt into the darkness at bedtime?

Phel's bed had been slept in only twice during the past week, and on both those occasions he had come in after she was asleep and departed before

she awakened in the morning. Gabe had no idea—
and no intention of asking—where he stayed on the
other nights.

Turk's uproarious laughter intruded on Gabe's
reflections, drawing her attention to the wall of
tongue-and-groove cedar logs that had already
risen to waist level.

She watched from the distance as Elmer
squeezed a ribbon of caulking into the long groove
of the log, then, with Turk's assistance, placed the
grooved cutaway bottom so it fit smoothly onto the
log beneath it.

She had learned during her year of study at the
State Technical Institute near Oslo, Norway, that
this method was far superior to the old practice of
placing round logs on top of each other with
caulking between them. This way, when the building settled the logs would form an impenetrable
wall, sealing out the moisture which was the major
cause of rotting.

Wishing she had been more successful at con-
structing a barrier to keep Phel from intruding on
her thoughts, Gabe turned to join the men. As she
approached them, Turk's voice rose in boisterous
teasing.

"Man, I'm getting about as lonesome as a bull
moose halfway to mating season!" Gabe ignored
his bawdy comment as she climbed the mound of
dirt and jumped up to the subfloor.

"If the boss lady doesn't give me some time off
pretty soon so I can go into town to do some
romancing, I might not be responsible for my
actions," he complained loudly.

Elmer nudged Turk to make him aware of Gabe's

presence, but the gregarious young carpenter ignored the warning. "I'm liable to attack the very first female that comes near me," he threatened.

Gabe flushed a little, but pretended to be unruffled at the implication of his words. "If you do I'll have to dock your pay for the time you spend goofing off," she reprimanded him lightly. "There's time enough for flirting in the wintertime."

She took her tape measure from her pocket and checked the height of the wall. "When the work's all done you can stay in bed until the snow melts in the spring, for all I care—as long as you don't do it on my payroll."

"Sounds great, if I don't have to stay in bed alone!" Turk guffawed loudly at his own joke as he sashayed off.

Gabe's answering chuckle was cut off in a gasp as she turned to encounter Phel Cannon's scathing gaze. The naked contempt in his eyes was apparent to her even before he spoke. "You seem to make a habit of leading men to expect capitulation from you at some later date."

Gabrielle glared at him for a full minute before she trusted herself to respond to his accusation. "Only a fool could misconstrue what I said to you in that regard."

"Only a *bigger* fool would misinterpret what you just said to your hired hand," Phel responded with equal animosity. "It's all right to fool around with the boss as long as you don't expect to get paid for it!"

"Why, you . . . Damn you, Phel Cannon!" she cried, her anger exceeding the shaft of pain his words sent through her. "Why don't you just keep your dirty thoughts in whatever cesspool they spring from?"

She wheeled about and jumped to the ground, ignoring his gruff reply. Whatever his angry words were, Gabe shut them out as she fled to the cabin before he could see the tears that blurred her hazel eyes.

Why did he have to be so exasperating? His behavior was as unpredictable as a spring storm. How could he pursue her friendship, courting her so assiduously, and then turn on her like a viper at the least expected moment?

On the porch Gabe unbuckled her heavy leather carpenter's apron and let it drop from her slender waist. The burden that bowed her shoulders was not so easily shed. She stood for a few moments longer, struggling to gain control over the hurt and anger that washed over her.

Phel's remarks had slashed more deeply than she cared to admit, even to herself. If they had been deserved it might have been a different matter. But she had always been scrupulously careful to observe a businesslike attitude toward her employees, even though it was difficult to maintain that reserve on a daily basis without appearing stiff-necked.

True enough, Elmer and Turk did tend to treat her like one of the boys, but neither of them presumed upon their relationship and she seriously doubted if either of them would knowingly attempt to alter it.

Still seething, Gabe opened the door to the cabin, half hoping to find it empty even though it was only midmorning and Marlene seldom left until after the noon meal. A cheery song coming from the bathroom soon disabused Gabe of her hope that she might find the solitude she craved.

She slumped into a chair and rested her elbows on the table, pressing her fingers to her throbbing temples. Marlene's trilling voice hushed suddenly as she came back into the room to discover she was no longer alone.

"Gabrielle, what's wrong?"

Gabe winced at the concern in the young girl's voice. She really didn't want to discuss her bout with Phel.

"Do you have a headache?"

"You could say I have a pain." Gabe grimaced. "But I would place it in another part of the anatomy."

Marlene shrugged, not comprehending Gabe's meaning. "I just made a fresh pot of coffee. Would you like some?"

"Sure." Gabe waited silently until Marlene had poured them each a cup of coffee, then joined the girl at the little table.

"Is it anything I can help you with?"

Gabe sighed. She was reluctant to confide in the girl when she didn't know what Marlene's involvement with Phel might be. After all, he had said she was "much more than just a housekeeper" to him. Still, the sympathetic look on Marlene's face invited confidence. "Not unless you're an expert at handling impossible men!"

"Oh, no!" The petite brunette laughed. "I don't know anything at all about men."

"Smart girl," Gabe approved. "As long as you

don't get mixed up with them you don't have to put up with their highhanded ways and ridiculous assumptions.''

"It sounds like someone has really been giving you a bad time.''

Gabe looked at Marlene's sweet, unlined face, wondering if she'd ever suffered the lash of Phel Cannon's angry tongue. It didn't seem likely that the girl's submissive nature would rankle him as Gabe's own independence apparently did. The words she'd bitten back tumbled to her lips.

"I've met some chauvinistic, macho men in my time but this one takes the prize. He makes me absolutely furious.''

"Why don't you fire him then?''

Gabe stared at her, a blank look on her face. "Fire him? Who . . . ?''

"Whichever one it is who's giving you trouble.''

"I wish it were that easy,'' Gabe snorted. "I'm talking about the 'Lord of the Island' himself. The only one who might get run off is me—when I flip my lid!''

"But . . . Phel?'' Marlene was incredulous. "You *can't* be talking about Phel!''

"I certainly am.''

"But Phel is the most wonderful person I've ever known!'' Marlene cried in disbelief. "I can't believe he'd do anything to annoy you!''

"I'm afraid it's a bit more than just annoyance. I'd like to wring his neck.''

Marlene gasped, her face shocked, her turquoise eyes widening in astonishment. "You can't mean that!'' She shook her head in denial, as though that would change the meaning of the words that had suddenly charged the air in the tiny cabin with electricity.

"Oh, I'm well aware that you think he's Mr. Perfect." Gabe's voice was matter-of-fact, not unkind. "But I can't help but assume you haven't been around enough to be able to accurately judge a man's character."

"I've known him long enough to know all I need to know." Marlene jumped to her feet, her voice rising shrilly so it lost its charming girlish quality. "He's a man of strength and conviction."

"I translate that to mean he's as stubborn as a mule."

Marlene stamped her foot in anger. "It's despicable of you to say that. And I thought you were such a nice person!" Her anguish was so real that Gabe was stricken to think she'd been the cause of it. Perhaps the girl was so smitten with Phel that she couldn't bear to hear anyone else's more objective opinion of him.

"Marlene." Gabe strove for a calmer tone. "I'm sorry if you're offended by what I said. The matter isn't important enough to me to be willing to have you hurt over it."

With an uncomfortable pang Gabe wondered how deeply the distraught girl would be wounded if she knew the real reason for the constant animosity between herself and Phel Cannon. She thought not only of that first evening when their emotions had erupted in a shower of pyrotechnics, but of Phel's persistent pursuit of a return engagement.

Through glistening eyes Marlene looked at Gabe in distress. No, Gabe decided, she couldn't risk telling the girl just how misplaced her loyalty was.

"I don't expect you to understand just how devoted I am—and all my family is—to Phel," Marlene quavered. She dashed a hand impatiently across her eyes and seemed to gain some control over her emotions. "We owe my father's life to him. And any one of us would fight for him without hesitation—no matter *who* said something bad about him."

Taken aback by the other girl's intensity, Gabe murmured soothing words. "I really didn't mean to get you so excited. I still don't—"

Marlene raised her chin and looked squarely at Gabe. "I want us to be able to be friends, Gabrielle. But you have to understand that I simply won't allow anyone to say anything derogatory about Phel."

"That I do understand. You've made that perfectly clear." Gabe's voice held the barest hint of humor. Becoming more serious, she asked, "Would you like to tell me about your father?"

"It happened two years ago," Marlene began as she sagged limply into her chair. "My father was a logger. In case you wonder where I learned to cook, it was by helping my mother cook in a logging camp."

Gabe thought impatiently that Marlene was getting sidetracked from her story. She prompted the girl to go on.

"Phel was at the camp, way back in the mountains, to arrange for some timber sales on some property he was buying in Montana. That was when he still lived in California."

Gabe nodded as the young housekeeper hesitated. "There was no doctor in the camp, only a nurse, when the accident happened.

"My father was helping a truck driver secure a load of logs. When the driver threw the first chain over the load, the top log was dislodged." Her eyes brimmed over again as her voice echoed the memory of an earlier horror.

"Dad was crushed under that huge log. They had to lift it with a crane." Marlene's voice broke and it was a moment before she was able to resume her commentary. "Mother and I were watching . . . we were so helpless. It was horrible."

Gabrielle patted the younger girl's hand sympathetically, wishing she knew just what to say.

"He was terribly hurt, groaning and crying; he begged for someone to do something. Of course the nurse was only able to give him an injection to ease the pain. We knew he would die if we didn't get him to a hospital immediately."

"Is that where Phel comes into this?"

Marlene nodded. "While everyone else was discussing where to go and how they should get him there, Phel ran to the little airstrip in the meadow. He broke a window to get into the hangar office to find the keys for the camp superintendent's Cessna."

Even having known Phel so briefly, Gabe still had no trouble envisioning the chain of events that Marlene described. He wasn't the kind of man who would wait for permission to act in an emergency.

"Phel just commandeered the airplane and flew Daddy to a hospital in Missoula," Marlene said with awe and tremendous respect in her tone. "Of course, when the camp super got back there was no need for explanations. Phel's quick action had saved my father's life."

"I understand now why you hold him in such high esteem," Gabe said softly. "I'm sorry I upset you with my outburst. I guess I was just overreacting to his criticism."

Indeed, Gabe conceded to herself, she had been defeating her own purpose by allowing herself to be drawn into a sparring match with Phel. She really didn't want to engage herself in a battle with the man she was under contract to for the rest of the summer. But neither would she allow him to make unwarranted attacks on her personal behavior.

It would behoove her to attempt to repair the rift before it widened and made her work all the more difficult. She was mature enough to admit—now that she'd had time to cool off—that their mutual flare of temper was probably prompted more by their uneasiness with each other than by any real difference of opinion.

Still, it rankled her to remember how quickly he'd misconstrued the meaning of the easy banter and endless hazing that any carpenter—male or female —considered a routine part of the job.

"How about some more coffee?" Marlene interrupted Gabe's meditation.

"Half a cup, please." Gabrielle smiled at the other woman. "Then I have to get back to work."

"Boy, you sure have a tough boss."

Gabe's laughter served to lighten the moment and remove a little of the tension from the air. "The worst I've ever had," she agreed.

"Gee, I have the best boss I've ever had," Marlene responded. "I guess I'm just lucky that Phel's earlier experience with women didn't make him hate *all* females."

As soon as the words were out Marlene covered her mouth in a gesture that spoke of her dismay at her own careless utterance. Nervously she smoothed down the billowy skirt of her pink-and-white candy-striped dress. "Now I guess you're going to expect me to explain that."

Gabe shrugged her shoulders expressively. "You *have* aroused my curiosity."

"I don't want you to think I'm used to gossiping." Marlene was clearly embarrassed. "My mother would kill me if she knew I told. . . ."

"Then say no more."

"There's not much more I *can* say. I don't know why I said that when I don't actually know anything about it."

"If you're trying to confuse me you've succeeded."

"I'd explain if I could. Really, Gabe, I would. I would trust you with anything." Gabe could see that the girl was itching to impart further information, despite her denial. She waited without asking to be taken into Marlene's confidence, sure that she would be.

"You see," Marlene expounded, "after the accident Phel and my folks became good friends. He's told them lots of things about his life—about his marriage."

Gabrielle almost gasped, so stunned was she by those words. Of course, she reasoned, a man seldom got to be forty years old *without* getting married unless he resembled a gargoyle—and Phel was certainly an attractive man.

Somehow, the thought of Phel married to some other woman was definitely unsettling.

"I've only heard little bits and pieces of conversation, so I really don't know what Phel's ex-wife did to him, but it must have been pretty terrible."

Gabe sat silently digesting Marlene's words. "I've often wished I knew what they were talking about," the girl admitted naively. "Anyway, I've heard Phel say it was years before he got to where he would have anything to do with a woman again." Marlene blushed prettily. "He says *I'm* partly responsible for that."

Gabe didn't wonder that this sweet-tempered, wholesome girl had something to do with Phel's learning to associate with women again. With a curious little ache in her midsection, she thought that Marlene, with her unstinting devotion, would certainly restore any man's faith in the fidelity and constancy of a loving woman.

Still deep in her reflections, Gabe thanked Marlene for the coffee and excused herself to return to work. Outside, she looked over the job site, noticing that the Eagle was no longer moored at the dock. She was relieved to discover Phel's absence from the island; it would allow her time to mull over the different facets of his personality as revealed by Marlene.

Her feminine curiosity was already burning. What *had* happened in Phel's marriage that had been so terrible? Had it had anything to do with the reason he'd chosen to become a virtual hermit, building a fortress on this secluded island?

Perhaps a knowledge of his past would enable her to sort out the complexities of his nature. It occurred to Gabe that until now her absorption in her own physical response to Phel had all but smothered her normal intellectual curiosity about him. It was a little disconcerting to realize that she'd spent almost every evening for the past three weeks with him and she still knew virtually nothing about him.

It would be to her own advantage to learn more about what made him tick—so she could avoid any future confrontations that would only drain her of the energy she needed to complete the job.

Of course, that would mean being more receptive to his friendly overtures. She could hardly expect to discover what provoked his seeming dislike of her at the most unexpected moments if she continued her chilly treatment.

Still, she told herself, it was only for a short time, so she could afford to be a little more flexible. When the house was finished in the fall she would move on to another job, ending their acquaintance. The thought brought an expression of dismay to her face, in spite of the fact that she would have laughed at anyone who suggested that their relationship could ever become a permanent one.

When she did give her heart again—sometime in the future—it would only be to a man of Buddie's sweet temperament and gentle nature, not to someone of Phel's mercurial passions.

An insistent little voice inside her reminded

Gabrielle how the volatility of Phel's passions had sparked an answering heat in her own body, in total disregard of their inherent differences.

Vowing to be wary of any possible entanglements that might develop as a result of her new curiosity about Phel, she reminded herself steadfastly that she had known within moments of their first meeting that she and Phel Cannon would mix as well as oil and water—not at all.

6

The pale blue lines blurred together as Gabrielle's thoughts strayed from the drafting pad on her lap. It was difficult to concentrate on structural details with the competing splendor of a jewel-like lake reflecting coniferous forests, magnificent mountains and puffy clouds.

The picture was framed by seventy-foot-tall pines, the needles so dark a green that they looked almost black in the shadows of a dark cloud directly overhead.

Across the lake a narrow band of beach was all that separated the fir, hemlock, cedar and pine from their mirror image in the water.

Gabe wondered if the gray clouds piling up over the mountains signaled a change in the weather. The preceding week had been uncomfortably warm. She'd given Turk and Elmer the day off because she'd noticed them slowing down on the past few hot afternoons.

She had been tempted to work on through the weekend and take a few days off later while they waited for the subcontractor to complete the electrical work. Instead, she'd recognized the men's need for some rest and relaxation, even though she felt no such need herself.

Returning her attention to the job at hand, Gabe studied the dimensions of the huge basalt-rock fireplace which would dominate the living room. Only the night before she'd learned of Phel's collection of western bronzes by such noted artists as Charles Russell and Frederick Remington.

She had taken advantage of the quiet hour after dinner in which she'd found herself alone with Phel to engage him in a conversation which she hoped would help her to discover more about his past.

It was then that she had discovered his interest in art. He needed little prompting to drag out several large cartons from where they were stacked in a corner. Delving into the packing, he brought forth an eighteen-inch-high bronze masterpiece by Russell of a bucking bronco and rider. A smaller piece followed, a museum-quality replica of Remington's "Mountain Man." Similar sculptures portrayed a calf-roping scene, several stalwart Indian chiefs and a majestic buffalo.

After exclaiming over a delicate hummingbird hovering over a columbine and some lifelike waterfowl crafted in bronze by contemporary artists Divita and Copenhaver, Gabe asked Phel where he intended to display them.

"To tell the truth, I haven't planned that far

ahead," he confessed. "The Montana Historical Society would like me to endow a permanent exhibit of the pieces I have. Maybe someday I'll do that, but for the present I'd like to enjoy them myself."

After searching her mind for a perfect location for a display cabinet, Gabe had come up with the idea of incorporating stone shelves into the fireplace, with lighting placed to highlight each individual piece. Phel had enthusiastically endorsed the project and asked if she could modify the plans before the stonemasons began work on the fireplace which would rise twenty feet to the top of the oak-beamed cathedral ceiling.

When she'd dismissed Turk and Elmer that morning Gabe had been burning up with excess energy and an eagerness to look over the fireplace plans. She'd assured them that she had no time to indulge herself by spending the day in town. And privately, she remembered Turk's recent declaration of his intention to go woman chasing at the earliest opportunity, so she didn't want to put a damper on his masculine pursuits by tagging along.

Gabe's thoughts were interrupted by the roar of the cabin cruiser cutting into the silence. She watched Phel from her high viewpoint as he stepped onto the dock and made fast the mooring lines. As he approached the porch where she was seated, she dropped her gaze to the drafting pad in her lap.

"I thought you were taking the day off," he greeted her.

"It seems that I am whether I want to or not," she responded, showing him the sparsely detailed drawing. "I thought I could sit out here to work so I could enjoy the view at the same time. But my concentration appears to suffer when presented with such a tempting distraction."

"Perhaps distraction is just what you need," Phel suggested. "You've been driving yourself pretty hard the past three weeks. Why don't you take the rest of the day off and do a little exploring?"

"I'm afraid I've missed the opportunity to do that today. I've already let Elmer and Turk take the pickup into Polson."

"That's no problem," Phel assured her. "If you don't mind roughing it, I have a cycle stored in my garage on the opposite shore. I use it for shore trips. You could probably learn to ride it easily. Then you could ramble around the hills or go into town whenever you like."

Gabe suppressed the temptation to boast about how well she could ride, and how she and Buddie had trailed across Canada on a motorcycle for an entire summer. Perhaps if she allowed Phel to become her instructor—if they spent a few comradely hours exploring the wilderness together—they might mend some of their differences and establish a more comfortable working relationship.

After all, she told herself, friendship and common interests were the most logical antidote to the sexual tension that had flared between them from the first moment of their meeting. Surely a few playful hours biking would help dispel some of the sensuous attraction that threatened to overwhelm them each time they were alone.

A smile of anticipation spread across her face. "I can't think of a more delightful way to spend the afternoon. Maybe by the time I get back I'll be more inclined to settle down and iron out the details for the bronze display."

Half an hour later Phel tied up the rowboat on the opposite shore and handed Gabe up onto the dock. He fished in his pocket for a key ring and nodded toward a small garage that was almost hidden by the trees around it. Gabe watched eagerly as he raised the door to reveal a shiny black-and-chrome BMW motorcycle.

"After you've had a few lessons and feel you can handle the cycle by yourself, I'll have a key made for you."

Gabe bit her lip, already wondering if she'd been wise to deceive him when she could so easily have admitted that she already knew perfectly well how to ride it.

A thrill of excitement and anticipation raced through her veins as the motor growled to life at the first downward stroke of Phel's booted foot. She needed no encouragement to mount the bike behind him. A long forgotten feeling of companionship engulfed her as her arms automatically encircled Phel's waist and they became almost as one.

With a lurch that forced her to cling tightly to avoid being thrown off, he revved the engine and sped onto the dirt road. Her mind only on the glorious feeling of freedom that riding had always engendered in her, Gabrielle leaned against Phel's broad back, pressing her face into his shoulder blade to evade the swirl of dust drifting up from the wheels.

Almost instantly Gabe became aware of her body's response to Phel's proximity. To her alarm she could feel her nipples harden against the pressure of his back. Arching away, she balanced in what was now a precarious position, moving her hands to his shoulders to allow a little space between them.

Just as she attempted to move back an inch or so on the seat the cycle hit a huge pothole, bouncing Gabe off in a flying tangle of arms and legs. Instinctively she rolled herself up, tucking her face into her knees for protection as she slid into a bed of pine needles.

Phel was at her side so fast that the wheels were still spinning on the cycle where he'd dropped it to the ground without pausing to set the kickstand.

"Are you okay?"

"No!" Gabe burst into a gale of laughter. "My dignity will never be the same."

"Maybe I should have told you that the first thing you have to learn is to hang on."

Gabe flushed in embarrassment, hoping Phel would attribute her discomfort to the spill and remain unaware she'd only taken the tumble because she'd been trying to turn off her sensual response to his nearness. At least the fall into the pine needles had served to accomplish that purpose.

Rising, she picked a piece of brownish-colored moss from her pale mint-green sweater and brushed pine needles from her jeans. "Maybe you could start a little slower next time."

"How about you taking the controls? I'll just ride along behind to help you balance the weight; you can choose whatever speed is comfortable for you." At Gabe's look of indecision he added, "It's really not that hard to do. The road levels off just over this rise, so it won't be so rough."

Feeling a little ashamed of herself for her deception, but secretly pleased at her convincing performance, she listened attentively as Phel explained the mechanics of starting the cycle and keeping it upright. Just as he had promised, the trail soon widened and leveled out so she had no trouble moving along at a moderate rate.

Each time they hit a bump Phel's hands were there to steady the handlebars until he was sure she was in control; then they returned to rest disturbingly on her upper arms. Why couldn't she restrain her reaction to Phel's touch? she wondered in agitation. Her heart began to pump furiously as his hands roved over her shoulders, caressing her neck so gently that she could feel gooseflesh rising under his fingertips.

So violent was her reaction when his lips brushed the base of her neck that the cycle began to wobble dangerously. She could hear a chuckle deep in his throat as he gripped the handlebars to straighten their course. To her distress, his lips continued to hover too close for comfort. She could feel his warm breath just behind her ear and she had to fight an inclination to lean closer to his mouth to make the contact complete once more.

To conceal the agitation Phel's feathery kiss had wrought Gabrielle increased her speed and made an effort to concentrate as she negotiated the winding trail. Phel's hands were busy again, moving over her back to her waist as he sat easily astride the seat. With his superior size and weight he had no need to cling as she had.

So distracted was Gabe by this time that she was actually seeking out the rough spots in the trail rather than avoiding them, hoping the diversion of a rougher ride would force Phel to keep his hands on the handlebars and his mind on the journey.

When his hands slid under her sweater Gabe turned slightly to protest, but her objection was blown away on the wind. If Phel heard her at all he paid no attention, for one of his hands moved up to cup a taut breast. To her chagrin, the nipple hardened at the touch of his fingertips. Frantic over her response, Gabe let go of a handlebar and tugged at his arm, at the same time trying to hold her course with one hand as the cycle hit a series of ruts.

In order to keep the bike upright Phel had no choice but to grasp the handlebar with his errant hand. But as soon as their movement was steady once more he returned to his exploration. Torn between her anger at him for taking advantage of her inability to stop him and the pleasure he was evoking as he stroked her fluttering stomach, Gabe turned her head and raised her voice again.

"You're going to make us crash!"

Phel's only response was to pop open the snap at the front of her waistband and slide down the zipper of her jeans. Gabe shivered violently as his fingertips caressed her quivering abdomen, sending waves of electric shock radiating out from his touch.

Wavering with indecision over whether to stop or speed up, Gabe chose the latter option, revving the cycle up to speed over a series of dips and curves in the trail. When she doubled their speed Phel had no choice but to hang on with both hands.

Bouncing over the ruts, the cycle zoomed along with Gabe in full control. She felt a rising exhilaration when Phel shouted at her to slow down. She knew she was traveling at a dangerous speed since she had no knowledge of the trail ahead, but she was driven by a devilish need to flee from the erotic impulses Phel had sparked with his touch.

When she was suddenly confronted with a Y in the trail Gabe wavered for an instant before choosing the branch to the right. Just as she topped a little rise Phel gripped the handlebars and wrestled control away from her tiring arms.

After a moment of struggling, she looked up to see that the path ahead of them ended abruptly in a little clearing that sloped upward away from the narrow trail.

Momentum carried the cycle and its passengers halfway up the incline, even though Phel's spontaneous reaction had been to cut the engine. After skidding to a stop the cycle leaned almost to the mossy ground before Phel's foot came down to stop their fall.

Gabe bailed out, hitting the soft, grassy hillside on her hands and knees. She jumped up and started running, fastening her jeans as she ran, with Phel only a hairs breadth behind her.

"You crazy fool!" he berated her loudly. "You could have killed us both!"

Gabrielle saved her breath for climbing the slope, knowing instinctively that she needed to put distance between them until Phel's temper had cooled down. She grasped a slender aspen sapling, pulling herself up over a large boulder just as Phel's hand grasped her ankle.

"Just wait until I get my hands on you," he threatened.

Kicking free of his grip, she scrambled over the rise, then made the mistake of turning to see how close he'd come. Her breath was coming in painful gasps as she wheeled about, right into Phel's arms.

Before she could act he pulled her to the ground, throwing himself on top of her. His lips ground into hers as he asserted his mastery over her. Gabe struggled to throw him off, but soon realized that her efforts were wasted, as he had no intention of letting her go. His mouth evoked an eager reply from hers as her lips parted to admit his demanding tongue.

Gabe allowed herself a few delicious moments to savor the heady sensations racing through her before she heaved her body upward in an attempt to throw Phel off. She thought she was free of him when he began to roll sideways down the far side of the slope, but he was quicker than she'd expected. He latched onto her arm, tugging her along in his downward plunge.

She didn't know whether to laugh or cry out as they rolled together, one over the other, to the edge of a small grassy clearing. After landing in a heap of tangled limbs, they lay quiet for a moment, trying to catch their breath. Phel's eyes brimmed with unspoken questions as they looked deeply into Gabe's. She caught her breath in wonder as his mouth descended to cover her own once more. A gurgling laugh was snuffed out at its source as desire once more flushed her entire body, leaving room for no other emotion.

Gabrielle found it difficult to breathe, so intense

was her reaction when Phel kneed her legs apart and settled there, arousing her dangerously, her desire matching his own obvious fervor. His hands were already at work unbuttoning the top button of her softly knit short-sleeved sweater.

"Do you think we should let them know we're here?"

The mirthful masculine voice spoke in an over-loud stage whisper. Gabe and Phel bolted up in unison, looking around them in belated curiosity.

The red-haired, heavily bearded man who had spoken leaned casually on the handle of his axe, exchanging looks of barely concealed amusement with his two companions. The youngest of the three, a boy of about sixteen, paused only a moment before resuming his task of stacking fire-wood on a small utility trailer. He appeared to be embarrassed by the whole incident.

"Sorry to interrupt you when you're so busy," the redhead chortled into his beard. "We'll be done loading up here in about ten minutes, if you'll just bear with us."

Phel and Gabe, who still looked about in open-mouthed bewilderment, scurried to their feet. "It seems *we're* the ones who're interrupting," Phel said with a courteous nod of greeting. "Please forgive our untimely intrusion."

With a gallant sweep of his hand he took Gabe's elbow. "Allow me to assist you, my dear. The children will be wondering what's become of us!" He winked boldly at the three of them before steering Gabrielle back up the grassy slope and over the rise.

When they reached the cycle, still lying on its side

where they'd abandoned it a short while ago, Gabe turned to Phel.

"You, sir, are a master of deceit." She glowered at him for a full minute before nudging him in the ribs with her elbow. "I like your style," she added with a chuckle.

"I could accuse you of keeping some secrets, too," he challenged as Gabe dissolved into gales of laughter.

With their arms about each other they sank helplessly to the mossy ground, oblivious to the chatter of a scolding chipmunk who didn't appreciate the rumbling bass chuckle and pealing feminine laughter ringing through the forested glade.

7

It was quiet on the island. No whining electric saws or pounding hammers broke the silence.

The walls were up, with new windows glittering brightly in the sunshine. The shake cedar roof was on. The interior walls were framed and waiting for the electricians to complete the wiring so the sheetrock and paneling work could begin.

Gabe and her crew were enjoying a much-needed holiday from their labors, a week-long respite that they all welcomed as they waited for the subcontractors to finish so their own work could proceed.

Gabe usually experienced an impatience at this stage of construction, when she had to worry about completion dates while she was forced to idle her crew and wait upon others.

Weeks of tension and hard work had taken their

toll on her, as well as the men. When Phel suggested that they all make a visit to Kalispell to attend the annual Big Sky Logging Championships, he didn't have to ask twice.

He'd conjured up a car—Gabe later learned that he kept it at the Tennysons' since he used it so seldom—and picked them up at the dock. After following a road that wound for miles through cherry orchards along the lake, they came to a broad, flat valley of patchwork wheat and hay fields.

Kalispell, Phel told them as they drove along, was named by the Pend d'Oreille Indians, and meant "Prairie Above the Lake." Gabe found that the little city of just over ten thousand residents was suitably named.

As they pulled into the bustling trade center of northwestern Montana, Gabe realized immediately that she'd have to adjust her preconceived notion of a tiny, backwoods town which served only a few loggers and miners.

Jovial residents and exuberant tourists alike flocked along the wide paved streets and sidewalks. Phel found a parking place in an alley so they could lunch at a small restaurant before driving out to the Flathead County Fairgrounds.

Sitting in the grandstand later, Gabe confessed her surprise to Phel. "This is a regular city," she said. "They have health-food restaurants, art galleries—even a summer playhouse."

"I know," he teased. "I've been here before."

"It's just not at all what I expected to find."

"Kalispell has changed its profile over the last couple of decades," he agreed. "A lot of the 'back to the earth' people found exactly what they were looking for here. The town has always been a trade center for this corner of Montana. But a newer element has been added that I can't explain. For some reason it's become an artists' colony, with potters, sculptors and painters of some renown settling here to work."

"That explains the big art center we passed."

Phel nodded. "Not only do they present exhibits, they also sponsor jazz concerts, ballet and repertory theater."

A loud whoop from Turk brought Gabrielle's attention back to the arena below. Two gigantic loggers were squared off in an axe-throwing contest.

Throughout the competition Turk kept up an excited commentary on the two men's skills. That he itched to get into the action was apparent to his friends.

"I'd take on either one of those guys if I got a chance," he boasted.

Phel's mouth twitched at the corner. "If that's what you want, just go to the Loggers' Ball tonight. There's almost always someone looking for an unadvertised event."

Turk blinked in surprise. "Oh! You mean fighting? I was talking about matching skills, not trying to get myself killed."

"Turk's not a fighter, he's a lover!" Elmer crowed, nudging the younger man with his elbow.

"That's the truth!" Gabe laughed. The smile dropped from her lips as she turned to find Phel glowering darkly at her.

"Oh, look," she cried, seeking to divert Elmer

and Turk's attention from Phel's angry countenance. "They're starting the tug of war!"

A few hours later the sound of power saws was still ringing in Gabe's ears as they left the fairgrounds. She was tired from the long afternoon in the sun and would have suggested returning to the island, but she knew Turk and Elmer were still bristling with pent-up energy.

Phel put his hand under Gabe's elbow and steered her to the car. "No visit to Kalispell is complete until you've been to Moose's Saloon. It's a real old-time Montana cowboy bar."

"I'd be more interested in something to eat," Gabe said as she climbed into the car.

"Okay, we can get a couple of pizzas at Moose's."

Wondering if pizza was now the standard fare at cowboy bars, Gabe assented.

"I hope you mean a couple of pizzas apiece," Elmer grumbled from the back seat.

The noise seemed to hit them in the face as Phel pushed open the swinging saloon doors and stood aside so Gabe could enter first. It took a minute for her eyes to adjust to the dim interior. Looking around at the celebrating patrons, who wore all manner of apparel, she decided that her own checked gingham western shirt with pearl snaps was quite dressy compared to the general assortment of tank tops and tee shirts.

Phel led them around several pool tables, found a booth, then went for a pitcher of beer. When he returned he squeezed in beside Gabe, crowding her into the corner.

Turk offered to go order the pizza so he could be

sure there was enough to satisfy his healthy appetite. "I'll go with you," Elmer insisted. "I want to be sure you don't put any of those nasty little anchovies on it."

Alone for the first time that day, Gabe and Phel looked at each other for a long, contemplative moment before her gaze fell to the table. "It looks like someone went crazy with a carving knife," she exclaimed.

"They say the sawdust on the floor comes from people carving up the tables," Phel said. Almost every inch of the table and booth was covered with initials, names and other less repeatable graffiti.

"You just haven't been around at all if your name isn't inscribed on a table at Moose's," Phel growled softly in her ear.

"Then I haven't been around." She shrugged. "And it looks as if I never will be—there isn't any room left to put it."

Phel examined the entire table, looking for a large enough space. Finally he took out his pocket knife and winked at Gabrielle. "Initials will have to suffice, I guess." With all the care of an engraver inscribing precious metal, he carved a tiny heart between two bawdy legends. Inside the heart he chiseled "P + G."

He laughed as he snapped the blade closed. "There, you're now linked with me in perpetuity."

Gabe's throat constricted as she detected an underlying intensity behind the casual remark. Her heart thudded loudly, seeming to come into her throat. "How many of these couples do you think were still together a month after they carved their names here?"

"A month?" Phel grinned down at Gabe. "A month can be a long time."

Gabe looked around, wondering why Turk and Elmer hadn't returned to the table. She thought of playing the jukebox for an excuse to escape the conversation, but it was already blaring a medley of loud rock hits. Still another preconception shot down, she thought. No western music, just good old rock and roll.

Spotting a bright red door marked "Wimmen," Gabe seized on the excuse to get away from the uncomfortable silence that had developed between them. Just as she drew even with the door she stopped to gaze into the glassy eyes of a bighorn sheep head mounted on the wall.

A little squeak of indignation escaped her lips as a huge hand patted her derriere. She turned to glare at a giant of a logger in a red plaid shirt, who apparently couldn't resist surreptitiously caressing Gabe's shapely hip. The logger was leaning against the wall, talking into a pay phone.

"Excuuuuse me." He bowed magnanimously and moved to let her by.

Turk and Elmer were already wolfing down huge slices of pizza by the time Gabe returned to the table. She slid into the booth and reached for her glass of beer. It had grown flat in her absence. She wondered inwardly how Phel would have reacted if he had witnessed her encounter with the logger. Maybe she was just imagining it, but earlier he had seemed to grow dark and threatening when she'd teased Turk about his prowess as a lover.

He really had no reason to act that way, she thought as she considered the situation. And yet she couldn't suppress a secret, very feminine sort of satisfaction at the knowledge that he had.

The noise level had risen so high that Gabe could scarcely hear Turk when he rose and said that he and Elmer were going to mosey around town for a while. Gabe finished her pizza, then looked at Phel, wondering if she should suggest a walk somewhere where it was a little quieter.

As though reading her mind Phel gripped her elbow and said, "Let's get out of here." They'd almost reached the door when Phel turned back to the table to leave a tip. Gabe paused for a second, then decided to go on out.

She'd just stepped through the swinging doors when she was grasped from behind, lifted off her feet and swung around.

"Hi, beautiful!" It was the burly logger she'd encountered on her way to the bathroom. "I just can't wait until the ball starts so I can dance with you." Gabe's head swirled almost as fast as her body as the logger lifted her and twirled her in a dizzy pirouette across the sidewalk.

"Put her down!"

Phel's words sounded like pistol shots. The logger staggered a little as he came too close to the curb and lost his balance. Still he didn't release her.

"If you value your life, put her down!"

"Oh, yeah?" the logger rumbled loudly. "Who says so?" He looked down from a good three-inch height advantage, a factor that Phel didn't seem to think worthy of consideration.

"I said, if you value your life you'll get your hands off her. She's *my* woman!"

Gabe felt the meaty arm about her waist slacken

as she was set gently on her feet. The giant at her side teetered slightly, shoving his hands into his pockets in a gesture of noncombatance.

"Sorry, friend," he said amiably. "Didn't know she was taken." He turned and pushed open the saloon doors, then waved a hand in farewell, as though parting from old friends.

Phel put an arm around Gabe's waist and guided her toward the car. "Let's see if we can find that crazy crew of yours so we can go home." Gabe just nodded wearily and followed him to the parking lot.

It seemed to Gabe that neither Turk nor Elmer stopped talking during the hour-long drive back to the lake. At least she was saved the necessity of contributing to the instant replay of the evening's entertainment.

They appeared to assume that she was asleep as she slipped into her own thoughts. "My woman!" The words echoed over and over in her mind. He had said, "She's *my* woman." The words cast a sudden illumination on the tangle of thoughts and sensations that had disrupted her peace of mind for the past month.

"A month is a long time," Phel had said earlier. And so it was. Long enough for her to fall in love with a man who bore no resemblance to the ideal she would have chosen for herself if she'd had her eyes open during the selection process. So myopic had she been that she'd failed to recognize until now what had caused her senses to erupt in violent surges each time Phel so much as touched her hand. Why had she assumed all this time that her physical yearning for him had no emotional basis?

So breathtaking was the sudden realization that Gabrielle felt her stomach muscles contract as though in a cramp. Why hadn't she noticed this attachment sometime during its developmental stages? When had the stinging discord that first marked their relationship evolved into this obsession to be with him? To be touching him?

But to love Phel Cannon was insane, Gabe reminded herself silently. There was no future in investing such deep feelings in a temporary relationship. In a scant six or eight weeks the house would be finished and she'd go back to Spokane for the winter.

Besides, she argued wordlessly against her new discovery, just because Phel had used a convenient ploy to ward off the logger's assault, that didn't mean there was any truth to his words.

But it *was* true; she knew it in her heart. If not for him, at least for herself. She was his woman. Somehow, in the past month, he'd stamped his brand on her, made her dependent on his nearness, whether intentionally or not.

Phel parked the car near the dock and the foursome crowded into the rowboat for the short trip across the water. As soon as they went ashore Gabe uttered a bemused goodnight to Turk and Elmer, hoping they would only think her sleepy. She went into the cabin, waiting quietly while Phel groped for matches and struck a light. Her face was pale and chalky in the harsh light of the lantern. Surely everything she was feeling must be written clearly on her countenance, she thought.

Phel busied himself with building a fire. The

flames felt welcome to Gabe, chilled as she was from a combination of her alarming thoughts and the cool night wind blowing across the lake.

When Phel settled into an easy chair and continued to stare thoughtfully into the fire Gabe excused herself and made for the bathroom. When she returned moments later she wore her pajamas, covered by a white corduroy bathrobe.

You'd think we've been married for twenty years, she thought wryly. Him seated in front of the fire, not talking. Me in my dowdy bathrobe.

A sudden shaft of longing gripped her as she pictured their life as it might be a scene of domestic tranquility. But would it be tranquil? Hadn't she and Phel locked horns within minutes of their first meeting? Didn't her independence goad Phel to lash out at her at the most unexpected times? Hadn't their month-long association been riddled with battle after battle?

And even when they weren't fighting, could she honestly refer to their relationship as tranquil? No, never, she thought, a blush creeping up over her cheeks as she recalled the ever-present passion that lurked just beneath the surface of their strained reserve.

To cover her agitation Gabe went across the room and pulled out the trundle bed, turned down the quilt and fluffed the pillow.

"Goodnight, Phel."

When he failed to reply Gabe took a few steps back into the room. "Thank you for giving us all a break from the island," she said softly.

"What?" Phel raised his head to look at her, looking almost puzzled at the interruption of his thoughts. "Oh, sure," he said in an offhand manner that made Gabe wonder if he'd even heard what she said. "Goodnight, Gabrielle."

Her soft goodnight was muffled as she fought to dispel the disappointment she felt at the brushoff. What am I doing? she asked herself once more. Why am I dreaming up some fanciful fairy tale of a love story? Why have I thought for a whole hour that something has changed between myself and Phel?

Hours later Gabrielle moaned and turned in her sleep. She'd tossed fitfully, trying to capture that elusive opiate, sleep. She'd finally drifted into a half dream state, too near the surface of wakefulness to gain any respite from her spinning thoughts.

Turning restlessly, she tossed aside the heavy quilt and felt it slip away to the floor. An unexpectedly cool breeze touched her face, prompting her to sit up and look around to see where it was coming from. After blinking a few times her eyes adjusted and she could see that the door was open.

A shadowy figure almost filled the portal as it lounged against the door frame.

"Phel?" Her voice was soft, questioning.

He came back into the room, pulling the door shut behind him. A moment later her bed sagged slightly with his weight.

"Are you having trouble sleeping too?"

Before she could frame a reply he turned to pull her into his arms. Gabe moaned a soft protest, moving to evade the butterfly touch of his lips as they trailed a gentle kiss along her hairline, a mere breath against her ear.

Then she turned back to him, seeking in the darkness, yearning toward the touch that evoked a rush of sensation . . . needing . . . wanting. . . .

She found his mouth, pressed it to her own hungry lips. A tantalizing male scent of musk filled her senses, a lingering whisper of Scotch. His tongue found unknown areas of sensitivity as it urged her own to join in this revelation, this process of discovery. She sighed, wanting more. Please . . . the word was unspoken on her lips as his kiss demanded more.

His hands were creating a magical response. First a gentle caress that smoothed her hair from her perspiring brow. Fingers—strong and bold, yet infinitely tender, searing a trailing path along a nerve that fluttered like a wild bird in her throat. Pausing, stroking a line from the shadowed hollow of her throat along her fine, delicate collarbone, hesitating until she thought she would cry out from wanting as he slowly unbuttoned her pajama top and pushed it aside.

His lips moved again, tasting, inciting a dizzying rush of need that mushroomed until it was overwhelming. His lips, at last, explored the exquisite lobe of creamy flesh, torturing the nipple that waited helplessly . . . desiring, straining upward to meet the mouth that closed on the bud, tormenting it, sending ripples of desire in ever-widening waves.

His hands trembled as they caressed the downy softness of her. His fingers probed further still, stimulating flames that blazed forth from the center of her passion, enslaving her in her need to learn more of him.

His voice, murmuring her name, was husky with passion as his lips sought hers again. He pressed the sweetness of his words into the soft, vulnerable corner of her mouth.

"God, you're beautiful!" His words were muffled against her delicately scented skin. "You're driving me crazy!"

"Hush . . ." Her fingers silenced him. She didn't want the words to dilute the fantasy, the erotic dream that was not really a dream, but a culmination of weeks of imaginings and longings.

Somewhere in her mind Gabe was trying to remember why it had seemed so important not to let this happen. But it was impossible to recapture the thought when his strong, demanding lips held hers captive and his arms nestled her close. He created a haven for her, a shelter from want, strong as steel, protective.

Gabrielle's lips parted in a soft sigh as she surrendered herself into Phel's keeping. Mentally, physically and psychologically her need to become his was so compelling that she was afire with it. She was caught up in a conflagration more consuming than a forest fire. Nothing could extinguish the fire, the longing, the flames licking, burning at her.

Too delicious, the kiss. Too intoxicating to stop.

And why, she asked herself now, should she want to stop? She loved him.

In spite of Gabrielle's tempestuous response, Phel seemed to be holding back, keeping a leash on his more primitive urges. His breathing was ragged and his large hands trembled with the effort of curbing his desire. When Gabrielle realized that he was steeling himself against the moment when she would draw away she spoke softly against his mouth.

"I want you, Phel." Her heart soared in expectation as she felt him catch his breath. "I need you as much as you need me."

His hands touched her reverently and she wondered for a moment if she'd really said the words out loud or if her heart had just spoken them inwardly. In moments their clothes were gone and he rose above her, supporting his great frame so as not to burden her too heavily as their bodies met. She arched to encompass him, to make him a part of her.

He came to her silently, swiftly, urgently, driven by his need to know her, rushing to a crescendo of melodic chords that blended delirium and reality into an explosion of thundering passion.

When he shuddered against her she couldn't prevent the whimper that escaped her lips through clenched teeth.

"Oh, no!"

Her involuntary cry was that of a hungry kitten snatched back from a bowl of warm milk after the first pleasurable mouthful.

He rose and gathered her trembling body into his arms and carried her to the larger bed. "Don't fret, sweet." His lips against the warm column of her throat promised, "I haven't drunk my fill of you yet."

Throwing aside the bedding, he leaned back against the pillows and pulled her on top of him. "There's much, much more, love." His kiss pledged an abundance of pleasure, inviting her to regain the momentum that had catapulted her to such breathtaking heights.

Gabrielle could feel her senses expanding to accommodate all the new luxurious perceptions Phel's touch conveyed. Her nerve endings vibrated in tactile response to his fingertips. The warm, masculine scent of him invaded her consciousness, filling her with a feeling of shared intimacy, a closeness she couldn't describe.

His skin had a slight tangy taste, her tongue discovered as it flicked across his chest, finding the male nipples in a nest of curly hair that tickled her nose.

Hands tangled in her hair, he forced her lips back to his own so he could drink fully the sweet nectar of her kiss. Her mouth felt swollen, almost bruised, and still she couldn't get her fill of his kiss.

When she thought she could bear the sweet agony no longer he guided her knees to his sides, tenderly urging her as her legs straddled his.

His lovemaking had built unimagined fires, flames that could only be extinguished by immersion into the maelstrom that preceded ecstasy.

The current was swift, inevitable, sweeping her along until she simply abandoned herself to the breathtaking rapids, swirling eddies, whirlpools without light or sound . . . until she was consumed in the darkness and the earth stopped spinning around the sun—for the sun was exploding in rapture.

She collapsed against his still-heaving chest, gasping, tremulous, surrendering to the languor of satiation as his fingers caressed her velvety skin.

"Phel . . ."

"Hush," he stilled her gently. "There's no need to say anything."

In darkness sleep crept over her, drawing a protective, silken curtain over her body, still damp with the fragrant dew of love, still entwined in the tangle of limbs that no longer ached with a long-unfulfilled need . . . no longer asked the night why it brought only an unsatisfied yearning.

8

If Gabrielle had set out to plan a perfect, dream vacation with an exciting, attentive companion, she couldn't possibly have envisioned an interlude of romantic splendor such as she enjoyed with Phel that week.

As though in conspiracy with the lovers, Elmer had appeared at the cabin door on Sunday morning to sheepishly remind Gabe that it was the Fourth of July and ask if he and Turk could take the pickup to Spokane for the week. They had to wait for the subcontractors now anyway, he reminded her, so they might as well be off her payroll for the duration. All they needed was transportation.

Gabe agreed without hesitation, wondering if they could detect her eagerness to see them depart. Phel pulled her into his arms the minute she closed the door.

"Now I have you at my mercy, woman," he growled into her tumbled hair. "Scream all you wish; no one will hear you."

"They're not gone yet." She giggled breathlessly, surrendering to his insistent mouth as he rained kisses all over her face. "What if they've forgotten something and come back?"

"They got their pay yesterday." He laughed. "What else could they possibly want? And Marlene won't be back till after the holiday, either." He met only a token resistance when he swept Gabe off her feet and carried her to the bed.

"I'm not screaming," Gabrille sighed as he began to undress her. As Phel's hands explored her curves she leaned back against the pillows and closed her eyes. "How come I don't feel awful this morning?" she asked, a little quaver in her voice.

"How come you thought you'd feel awful this morning?" The words were muffled as his mouth moved from her throat to a succulent nipple. Gabe shivered as his lips moved across her stomach, his tongue tracing a circle around her navel.

"Last night brought a great change in our relationship," she breathed, the words scarcely audible.

"Here's to great changes in our relationship."

The roar of a thousand oceans was in her ears as she arched her body spontaneously to connect with his searching mouth once more. The moan on her lips became a cry of pleasure as rivers of fire flooded her senses.

Wantonly her fingers tangled in the curly black hair at the nape of his neck, urging him to increase the pressure of his lips. In mounting excitement she moaned his name.

"Yes, love." His voice was husky with passion. "I'll give you anything you want, love."

"I want you, Phel." Her voice was no longer melodic but edged with urgency. "I want you now."

Even in his compulsion to take her he was achingly gentle, taking care not to overburden her with his weight. Tenderly he cradled her hips with his huge hands, delaying for an infinitesimal moment in an effort to still his primal hunger.

Eagerly Gabrielle rose against him to encompass her lover, driven by a need to be closer to him. Together they sought and found each other's most responsive places, he discovering and adoring all the contours of rounded softness, she delighting in the hardness of his rugged manhood.

No cue was necessary for either one to increase the tempo as their lips urged them to satisfy the need they created in each other. Kindled by a rapidly spreading flame, they surrendered to the pleasure, every pore and fiber of them steeped in the erotic stimuli of smell and touch and taste.

Every movement complementing another, they rose in rapture, touring the universe in cosmic splendor. In utter, consummate ecstasy they reached that exquisite plane where even pleasure is so intense that it can be borne no longer.

"Oh . . . don't . . . stop. . . ." Gabrielle's words tumbled forth in mindless confusion until she couldn't speak . . . couldn't breathe anymore.

* * *

For the first time in her career, Gabrielle handed the blueprints over to the electrical contractor, asked him to share the plans with the plumbers should they arrive in her absence and promised to check back in a few days to see how they were getting along. For the first time in more than three years she felt as though she honestly deserved a vacation and vowed to allow herself total freedom from the responsibilities of the job.

She and Phel explored the surrounding territory, often taking a lunch as they went roaring over the lakeshore trails on the BMW to find secluded picnic hideaways. Phel seemed to know all the hidden byways of the wilderness area. The swiftness with which he built their campfires spoke of a long kinship with the outdoors.

"You must have been a Boy Scout," Gabe surmised as Phel handed her a cup of freshly brewed coffee, then turned to adjust the spit on which their lunch was roasting.

"Actually, I was a Scoutmaster a lot longer than I was a Scout." With a little prodding from Gabe he admitted that he was still heavily involved with the program and spent many weekends training youngsters in woodsmanship at a nearby camp.

"There's a lot more to learn about the area we live in than just survival techniques." He explained his reasons for his devotion to the program. "Ideally, everyone should learn to enjoy the environment without endangering either themselves or the wildlife."

"Does that mean you don't advocate hunting?"

"Not at all," Phel said. "Hunting has its place.

Only last winter I joined a group of ranchers to track down a couple of cougars that were thinning out their livestock."

"Did you hunt as a boy?"

"Oh, I learned to shoot at tin cans, but there was never anyone around to show me anything beyond that, so I spent more time reading about it than I did doing it."

At Gabe's puzzled look he explained. "I guess there are lots of guys who grow up without a father around to do things with. But I always felt shortchanged because I didn't realize that when I was a kid."

"And so you're making up for that lack now by working with other kids who might have the same needs." Gabe had a sudden flash of insight into Phel's character. He seemed a little embarrassed by her admiration.

As time went by Gabrielle learned more about Phel's solitary upbringing as an only child whose father had left the scene before Phel was born. She was surprised to learn that he'd grown up in the area, a fact no one had mentioned when they'd alluded to his California residency.

"If you love the mountains and wilderness so much, what prompted you to go to California?" she asked one afternoon as they loaded the Eagle with food, suntan lotion and water skis.

"Money," was his curt reply. "I was tired of being a nobody."

"Oh, you can't have been a nobody!" Gabe protested. "Or ever have *thought* that about yourself."

"Apparently some people did." He grinned, but

the smile failed to reach the depths of his blue eyes. "I don't know if money makes that much difference, but no one treats me like a nobody anymore."

Gabe was sure that his own attitude and imposing presence had more to do with any deferential treatment he might receive than money did.

"Oh, poor baby!" she teased. "Nobody loves him just for himself." Her heart gave a funny little lurch. Could he see in her eyes just how overpowered she was by his virility and masculinity? How involved her emotions were now that he occasionally let her glimpse the hidden mellow sweetness under his steely exterior?

Was that the real Phel? she wondered. Or was she misreading him entirely? Perhaps her first perceptions of him had been correct. How could she sort out all the conflicting signals he sent her?

With Buddie she'd never had any doubts. He had always been as readable as a menu. All she'd ever had to do was ask for her desire of the moment.

Certainly Phel wasn't so pliable, but would it really have added to the strong attraction she felt for him if he had been?

Determined not to let such lingering doubts spoil the too-short interlude they were enjoying, Gabe forced a new gaiety to her laugh and sought to show Phel—by her eagerness to join him in each new venture—just how precious their time together was to her.

They boated to Polson for supplies, learning more about each other's tastes as they shopped together. They loaded up on film so they could take pictures of the bighorn sheep on Wild Horse, the largest island in Montana and home of the biggest herd of mountain sheep in the United States. Gabe squealed with delight when one of the less timid bighorns came up and snatched a folded brochure out of Phel's hip pocket and began to munch on it. Unfortunately, Phel was holding the camera at the moment, so they missed getting the picture of a lifetime.

Gabe found Phel's sense of humor enchanting. The hours passed so pleasantly; they flew by much too rapidly to suit her.

In the evening they built a campfire on the lakeshore and fried trout they'd caught for their supper. Phel spread a blanket and invited Gabrielle to join him to watch the sunset over the water, then proceeded to ply her with kisses so that neither noticed the lavish brushstrokes of color across the sky.

When their driving need for each other had been sated, they lay in each other's arms and pointed out the constellations in a heaven that seemed to Gabe to be designed for lovers.

They held a minor celebration on the day the underground utility lines were connected. Phel strung a long cord from the temporary service package to the cabin to hang a glaring light bulb over the table while Gabe prepared dinner. Halfway through the meal she stood up and pulled the chain to extinguish the bulb. Lighting the lantern, she laughed at their impatience with modern conveniences and leaned back to finish her food in the mellow glow of lanternlight.

Once she'd stacked the dishes in the sink she

joined Phel on a pile of pillows before the fireplace. They settled into a companionable silence for a while, listening to big-band music from a little transistor radio they'd bought.

It occurred to Gabrielle that this was the first time since they'd met that she and Phel had had any outside source of entertainment. So far, they had relied on conversation to fill the time they spent together.

"I wonder if we'll stop talking to each other now that the electronic age has arrived in the wilderness," she said in a tone of deep philosophical regret.

"No doubt," he sighed ponderously. "The life of stimulating drawing-room conversation as we know it is probably threatened with extinction even now. All it needs to deliver the mortal blow is the arrival of television on Wild Stag Island."

"Oh, no!" Gabe exclaimed in mock despair. "Surely you wouldn't ruin this island paradise with the trappings of city life! I thought that's what you were trying to get away from."

At Phel's silence Gabe turned toward him, leaning on her elbow to study him. He seemed to be fighting some inner conflict that made him almost unaware that she was still at his side. At length she moved to sit up, unable to bear the strained silence any longer.

"I guess I'll do the dishes," she said, hoping he would protest and keep her close to him.

But she knew she wasn't really close to him. Somehow her remark had caused him to withdraw from their camaraderie as surely as if he'd left the room. When she finished the dishes Gabe went about the business of getting ready for bed.

When she asked in her most suggestive voice if Phel were ready to come to bed with her, he rose and stretched. "If you don't mind I think I'll take a little walk before I turn in." Before she could ask if he'd like some company, he was out the door.

Gabe huddled in the big bed alone, trying to rid herself of a feeling of rejection by reminding herself that everyone needed a little private space to retreat to. She and Phel had spent so many hours in each other's company that week that it was no wonder he required some time alone, she told herself. But still she found it painful to know that he was so obviously troubled by something she'd said that he chose to exclude her.

It shouldn't have come as a total surprise to her, she knew. She'd run into the same reluctance to share the details of his personal life with her when the subject of his marriage had come up. She'd wanted to ask him so many questions, but he'd given her no chance to do so, saying curtly that it had only taken him a year to learn that matrimony spelled trouble.

Gabe had been quick to tell him how satisfying a good partnership could be. But even as she said the words she was seized with a feeling of disloyalty at the ones she had chosen.

For the first time since she was sixteen years old she paused to examine just what her relationship with Buddie had really been. Partner? Was that the way to think of her husband? Her mate? If not for a freak accident, the man of her choice, the man to spend her life with?

But perhaps that had been the secret of success in their marriage. So what if it hadn't been marked with the explosive passion she'd experienced with Phel. Wasn't the friendship, the deep, abiding affection they'd felt for each other a more solid foundation than animal attraction?

She *had* loved Buddie! His loss had turned her well-ordered world upside down—a disorder that had taken several years to right. *That* was real love. Not this soaring, albeit exhilarating expansion of the senses that she was experiencing with Phel.

And if this physical need, this craving, was simply a sort of love that was different than love as she had known it in the past, then which was the valid love? The tried and proven road to happiness? Or this bumpy, painful rollercoaster ride that sent her to the heavens only to plunge her to the depths of uncertainty?

Gabe wondered if the kind of love that left her so confused was the same sort of relationship that had led Phel to describe marriage as "not for him." Indeed, if tonight were a measure—a yardstick of the spectrum of feelings one could expect in such a passionate commingling—then perhaps it would be well to find out early on if she had the tolerance and staying power required for such a turbulent affair.

Berating herself silently for allowing herself to become infatuated with so ineligible a man, Gabe punched her pillow into a more comfortable shape and resolved to sleep on her inner conflict. Perhaps it too would have a more manageable shape in the morning.

When morning came the first thing Gabrielle was

aware of was a hard masculine RSVP to her torchy invitation of the night before.

She hadn't heard Phel come in when he'd joined her sometime after she fell asleep. During the night their bodies had gravitated toward each other, guided by that latent desire to cling together that was never far beneath the surface of their consciousness.

Now the long, hard angles of his frame curved to complement the soft contours of her femininity. As his fingers began to explore the curve from narrow waist to flaring hip, Gabe found that her ceaseless appetite for his lovemaking hadn't waned with her seizure of doubt.

As she listened, the deep, steady breathing of sleep became erratic, signaling the awakening of the man holding her tight. The automatic movements of the unconscious body became conscious and premeditated, designed to kindle the flame of sensuality until the heat couldn't be denied.

She turned in his arms to seek his mouth, giving herself over to the wild eroticism he awakened in her. Together they sought and found the most responsive areas of each other's flesh, delighting in the tingling sensations evoked by each stroking caress.

When she thought her senses would erupt in head-spinning rapture he gentled her like a skittish colt, holding her back, then whetting her appetite again until release could no longer be denied.

While Gabrielle was still shuddering in ecstasy he satisfied his own aching urgency, easing his fever in consummate ardor as he adored her with his body.

As he cradled her in his arms, sighing deeply, Gabe opened her eyes to examine the mouth that was just inches away. His smile betrayed the masculine tendency to exercise dominion over the female of the species. But now, softened by passion, his lips were also full and sensuous, undemanding, almost tender. His chin was shadowed by the night's growth of beard, blue-black along his skin.

Gabrielle was suddenly enveloped by a wave of tenderness. This man could be so lovable when his raw edges were softened by intimacy.

As she lifted her eyes to his, Gabe found that Phel was also engaged in studying her. "Your eyes are the same color as the Montana sapphires we saw at that gift shop in Polson," she said to cover her dismay at being caught in her inspection of him. Indeed, the blue was so deep that looking into his eyes was a little like climbing down into a well.

"Your eyes," he returned her compliment, "are as beautiful as a freshly caught speckled trout."

"Thanks a lot," she groaned as she pushed him away and sat up. "Let's hope for both our sakes that they're a little more fragrant."

Reaching to pull her back into his arms, Phel threw a leg over Gabrielle's thigh. "You don't have to be in such a hurry to get up," he enjoined. "Stay here and we'll see if we can discover any new erogenous zones."

Giggling breathlessly, Gabe squirmed out of his grasp. "It's too nice a day to spend it all in bed," she said. "The crew will be back tomorrow and I'll have to go back to work, so I want to do something today."

"That's precisely what I had in mind." Phel reached for Gabe again.

"Get up, pervert!" With a thrust of her pillow in his face, she wriggled free and escaped to the bathroom. All at once a feeling of happiness was bubbling up inside her.

All the doubts and misgivings of the previous night were dissipating in the warmth of their love-making. It drove away obstructions to her peace of mind just as the sunlight melted the morning fog from the meadow by the lake.

They drove north around the lake, through Lakeside and Somers to Bigfork, where they left the lakeshore to enter the Swan River Valley. They pulled over to the side of the road to watch a moose cow, knee-deep in water at the river's edge. The placid-eyed, half-ton animal mooed softly while water drops ran from her shaggy jowls. Sensing no threat from her observers, she lowered her huge head again to graze at the bottom of the river.

Several miles further along the road they passed an angler, up to his hip-waders in the stream as he cast his lure out over the water. He waved a cheerful greeting to the passersby before reeling in his line and casting again.

After turning into a narrow lane Phel pushed the accelerator down until the car bumped along at what seemed to Gabe an excessive rate of speed. "Where are we going?" she asked, puzzled by the impromptu change of course.

"Somewhere where I can have you alone," was his gruff response.

"What do you mean, alone?" she laughed. "In the past ten miles we've passed one lone fisherman and a moose, both of whom were wading in the river, minding their own business.''

"That's too many interruptions to suit me." He reached for Gabe with one hand, but had to grab the steering wheel again when the car lurched over a deep rut. "There's an old retired trapper just down the trail here who fits out hunting parties and trail rides. We'll get a couple of horses from him and spend the rest of the day in the hills—where we can be undisturbed.''

"But I can hardly ride!" Gabe protested, thinking that horseback riding was far from her strongest suit.

"That's all right. We'll see if Harvey has a Shetland pony you can ride.''

"In a pig's eye you will!" Her tone was indignant. "This is the dumbest idea I've ever heard.''

As though she had agreed to the outing, Phel buzzed along the graveled road until he came to a rustic little cabin with even more quaint outbuildings. A grizzled old man with a scuttling gait stepped out to meet them, waving a hand in greeting. When the two men had exchanged hellos and Gabe had been introduced, Phel asked about renting horses for the day.

Harvey Hammond suggested Gabe come into the house to meet his wife Stella. "Might as well have her put together a lunch for you while Phel and I saddle the horses," he suggested.

When they entered the kitchen Gabe was impressed by the cozy interior. It retained the look of a trapper's cabin but still boasted all the conveniences of a modern kitchen.

Stella greeted her guests warmly. She was a tall,

lanky woman in her late fifties, still handsome, with a blustery, outdoorsy look. She chattered about how hot the weather had been, how her vegetable garden was way ahead of the year before's, and asked about the progress on the new log home.

But as soon as the men went out her attitude changed abruptly and she immediately proceeded to inquire about Gabe's interest in Phel.

"Not that it's any of my business." She shrugged. "But we like to keep tabs on the boy to see how he's getting along." Her tone implied that he didn't always get along too well without such maternally inspired supervision.

"Phel has been nice enough to show me a bit of the countryside while my crew is off and we're waiting for the plumbing and electrical work to be finished," Gabe explained stiffly. "Tomorrow, when my men return, I'll be too busy to think about anything but finishing the job."

Stella inquired politely about what part of the work Gabe would assist with, raising an eyebrow when she was informed by her bristling guest that she worked on all phases of the construction and was considered by her colleagues to be an excellent finish carpenter.

"As soon as the house is finished, of course, I'll be moving on to the next job." Gabe felt a peculiar uneasiness in her midsection as she said the words. It was something she hadn't allowed herself to think about all week.

At the older woman's look of satisfaction Gabrielle wondered—not for the first time—why her own frame of reference where Phel was concerned was so different from everyone else's.

133

Her first impression of him had been a natural reaction prompted by his explosive anger. She saw him as a giant, overbearing man who was accustomed to having his will obeyed. And he had appeared to be prepared to resort to any tactics necessary when he failed to intimidate her into leaving the island and abandoning the contract.

Once she had convinced him that she was capable of building the house, he had become helpful and sometimes even supportive. But that was because, at that point at least, everything had been going the way he wanted.

Or maybe it was only because he had wanted *her!* She'd been aware since the first night she'd spent in the cabin that he was determined to seduce her. He had acted all along as if it were only a matter of time until he got what he wanted.

But why, she puzzled, did everyone else—particularly the women she'd met—act as though Phel were an innocent boy who needed to be protected? Marlene would do battle with anyone who thought ill of him, and Stella's attitude was that of a mother bear protecting her awkward but adorable cub.

Gabrielle looked up into Stella's bright-eyed stare and thought she detected a softening, a warmness that hadn't been there a moment ago. She probably likes me better now that she knows I'm only a temporary aberration, Gabe thought.

She was almost tempted to unload all her own uncertainties about her relationship with Phel on this gruff but tender woman who seemed to have the capacity to mother anyone she decided needed her attentions. But before she could speak again the door swung open to admit the two men.

Phel came directly to Gabe, his arm coming down over her shoulder as easily as if he always held her that way. "Are you ready to go?" His voice was tender and affectionate, with none of the teasing he'd shown earlier.

Totally confused by this unexpectedly open display of familiarity, Gabe raised her eyes to meet Stella's contemplative look, then ducked her head to hide her agitation. How could anyone expect her to explain her position in Phel Cannon's life when she didn't know herself? And why go to the trouble of defining the relationship when it was only temporary anyway?

"I've packed you a lunch," Stella said, her piercing eyes still examining Gabe. "Nothing fancy, but it should be plenty unless you intend to stay out for a few days."

"Oh, we can't," Gabe assured her. "My crew will be raring to go to work right after daylight tomorrow." Even as she said the words she thought they sounded a bit hollow. No doubt Turk and Elmer would be about as eager to end their vacation and return to work as she was.

With a profusion of thanks and promises to return before sunset, Phel and Gabe mounted the two sturdy old trail horses named—somewhat incongruously, Gabe thought—Hezekiah and Dorothy.

A leisurely ride took them across acres of meadowland where white-faced cattle grazed in little clusters. The land sloped gradually into the foothills, where they had to follow the trail cut by previous riders to make their way through the dense evergreens. They paused frequently while Phel pointed out different species of bird and game.

They followed the winding river, past deep green pools, until they found a shallow crossing. Pausing in midstream, they surveyed their magnificent surroundings. The scenic valley was nestled between the Mission Mountains and the Bob Marshall Wilderness area, where the mountains of the Continental Divide rose to nine thousand feet in spectacular Cambrian limestone reefs.

Gabe turned to find Phel absorbed with the shape of her leg. His hand came out to caress her thigh, moving up to the tender V where her legs met. Gabe's breath stopped short when she saw the glaze of passion in his eyes.

With a single motion his arm went around her, lifting her from the saddle to settle her in front of him on Hezekiah. The kiss, when it came, was long and breathtaking, and when Gabrielle raised her lips from his at last, the sun reflected brilliant prisms of light off the sparkling water, refracting blue glints in Phel's eyes as they studied her seriously.

"Have you ever made love on horseback?" His lips against her throat were creating an immediate need to experiment and see if such an innovation were feasible.

A whinnying complaint from Dorothy, answered by a lunging sidestep from Hezekiah, reminded them that they were still in the middle of the rocky stream bed. Phel took Dorothy's reins from Gabe and gave them a tug as he urged his own mount to move.

Gabrielle snuggled into the curve of Phel's arm and relaxed while the horses made their way precariously over the rocky sandbar that marked the center of the stream. "Shall we stop here?" she asked in a teasing voice.

Phel's arm tightened about her. "If I use all my manly strength and determination I might be able to wait until we get to that grove of trees on the opposite shore before I give in to the compulsion to make love to you."

While Phel tethered and unsaddled the horses, Gabe took a blanket from behind her saddle and spread it under an aspen tree, then stretched out on it.

"Why did I get the third degree from Stella?" Gabe couldn't restrain the question any longer.

Phel dropped down at her side and began an exploration of the bodice of Gabe's peasant blouse. "I guess Stella sort of adopted me when I went to work for them as a hunting guide one year when I was so broke I couldn't see my way through the winter. She's appointed herself to look out for me, to protect my interests."

Gabe pushed aside his questing hands and sat up. "She as much as asked me what my intentions are regarding you," she said indignantly. "It seems to me that if any questions are in order, they shouldn't be directed at me."

"Are you asking me what my intentions are regarding you, Gabrielle?"

Gabe's eyes questioned his, waiting to be told it was all right to be asking. When he didn't speak her gaze faltered. A painful lump rose in her throat.

"Right now my intention is to make love to you.

That's all I can think about. I want to make love to you until we're both weak and depleted. And then I want to rest for a while, and then make love to you again."

"Well, then," Gabe said tremulously, "what are you waiting for?" How could she deny a desire so intense that it blotted out everything else in the world? When that same primary need to join flesh with flesh raged within herself, the magnetism created was stronger than either of them could withstand.

The sun was disappearing behind the mountains when they returned to the trapper's cabin. Harvey hobbled out to extend Stella's invitation to stay for supper, but Phel just waved a hand at the rangy figure silhouetted in the lighted kitchen doorway and called out to him that they'd have to take a raincheck.

Gabrielle called a soft goodnight and a thanks for the picnic lunch, which she smuggled into the waiting car so no one would see that they had been so absorbed in each other that they had forgotten to eat it.

"Harvey and Stella never seem to change," Phel said, his voice warm with satisfaction.

"How long has it been since you worked for them?" Gabe was puzzled by Phel's remark about being so broke—when she knew he'd been prosperous enough to retire at an early age.

"Oh, it's been years." He smiled down at Gabe as she snuggled up against him, but somehow his eyes had become cold and remote. "I was only twenty-two at the time."

His tone had tightened until his voice was so strained that she scarcely recognized it. Sensing that she'd stepped across some invisible line into painful territory, Gabe sought to lighten the conversation.

"I knew it couldn't have been recently. Being broke doesn't exactly go with the rest of the present scenario. Was that before you learned the secret of success?"

"I guess you could say it was before I learned to hang on to what I had." Gabe was astonished at the bitterness the words held. She wished there were some way she could move backward in time for a few minutes and start the conversation all over again.

Phel's hands were clenched on the steering wheel. In the dim light from the dashboard Gabe saw how tense and strained his jawline was. She ran her fingers up along his arm and shoulder, stroking lightly over the pronounced tendons in his neck, hoping to reduce some of the tension in his muscles.

"If it was such a long time ago, must it still have this effect on you now?" she asked softly. "Isn't it time to dump some of that load if it's so painful?"

Phel's arm came around Gabrielle's shoulder in a swift, spontaneous hug before he patted her arm and then released her to return his attention to his driving. "You're very sweet, Gabrielle. And I appreciate your desire to make everything right for me. But this is something that can't be fixed with a few kind words. Nothing—not time or anything else—can fix it."

Gabe endured the strained silence that followed, aching to console the man who sat so close to her and yet had moved so far beyond her reach with a few words.

A quiet little voice in her subconscious urged her not to make any waves that might cause their fledgling relationship to flounder. To let the silence deepen until the subject no longer stood between them. She didn't know where she found the temerity to ask the question, to give voice to her guess.

"Do you think you're the only man who has found at the end of a marriage that his ex-wife left him with nothing?"

At Phel's gasp of surprise and outrage she knew that her shot in the dark had found its mark. Being sympathetic and understanding hadn't worked any miracles, she thought. Perhaps the brutal truth could accomplish what empathy couldn't.

"It always hurts to lose a loved one." Her voice was steady and unemotional. "I wanted to die when I lost Buddie. It can't hurt any more than that to lose one's sweetheart in any other way."

Phel's breath was ragged; she could feel his anger and frustration growing, filling the dim interior of the car. "There's no comparison!" he burst out. "Sure, you lost your childhood sweetheart and so did I. But that's where the similarities end!"

It suddenly seemed very quiet in the car, with only the sound of the smoothly purring engine and Phel's tense breathing breaking the silence. In a concerted effort to gain control over his emotions he drew several deep, steadying breaths before he spoke again.

"It wasn't just my bank account and all my other earthly possessions Amy took when she cleaned me out." His voice was harsh, but surprisingly calm. "When she left she took away something I could never regain. Something I had searched for and longed for all my life. I spent all my teen years writing letters and making long-distance telephone calls to try to find any trace that would lead me to my heart's desire."

Gabe's heart expanded in empathy and she made a soft sound that wasn't even a word to let him know she understood the depth of his emotion.

"From the day my mother died when I was twelve years old, I tried to find the father I had never known," he said in a strangled voice. "When I located him at last I found he didn't even know of my existence. I begged him to come out and spend some time with me and my new bride."

Gabe's hand covered Phel's on the steering wheel as he went on. "I didn't know when I went off to work each morning just how well Amy and my father had become acquainted during their long days together. I didn't find out until the day I came home and they were gone!

"I knew she was impressed by his success; at the age of forty he was a mature, handsome, worldly man. I must have seemed like a kid to her in comparison."

"Oh, Phel!" Gabrielle couldn't hold back her cry of shared pain. "How *could* she? How could *he?*"

"After a few years I found I could forgive my father for taking my wife," he said grimly. "You don't have to be very wise to figure out that if she were that easily led astray, anyone could have done it."

Gabe fought back the impulse to say just what she thought of a woman—no matter how youthful—who could be so faithless.

"But what I never could understand was how she could do that to me when she knew how much it mattered to me . . . how long I'd worked to bring about the reunion." Gabe shivered at the arctic chill in his voice. "She took away the one thing I'd wanted most in my life. All those years of my childhood when other kids had a father to take them fishing or to teach them how to pitch a baseball, I dreamed that someday I'd find my own father."

Gabrielle brushed away the tears that she hadn't noticed until now. She leaned her head against Phel's shoulder and wished she knew how to comfort him.

"It hardly mattered to me that Amy had emptied my savings account of what was left from my mother's life insurance," he said, all the old anguish fresh and alive again in his voice. "All that mattered to me was that she'd robbed me of the father I'd found at last."

9

With a heavy sigh Gabrielle turned off the airless sprayer and picked up a rag to wipe the paint thinner from her hands. Cleaning out the sprayer after its use was one of the more thankless, time-consuming parts of her job. She often likened it to cleaning up the kitchen. Although doing the dishes often took as much time and energy as the cooking, it seldom drew the praise earned by a well-prepared meal.

In the past two weeks the exterior of the house had undergone a noticeable leap toward completion. In order to stay out of the plumbers' way, the crew had concentrated their efforts on building the deck, installing the outside finishing touches, such as rain gutters, and applying the wood preservative that would prevent the sun's ultraviolet rays from weathering the wood.

After a couple of days of unbearable moodiness in which she'd found herself short-tempered with Elmer and Turk, Gabe had voluntarily isolated herself by doing tedious chores that kept her at a distance from the men.

Her solitude, and the time she spent dwelling on her own thoughts, had done nothing to improve her disposition. The day before, when she'd cursed roundly after cutting a board an inch too short, Elmer had even suggested she take a few days off and get away from the job if it was bugging her so much, an idea that gained in appeal with each passing hour.

Since the day Gabe and Phel had spent horseback riding in the Swan Valley, tension had been a tightly coiled knot keeping her nerves on edge. After their return that evening, Gabrielle had tried to induce Phel to talk out his long-endured frustration and anger, but she had soon learned that he'd already let down his defenses much more than was customary.

He had stubbornly refused to be drawn into any personal conversation until Gabe finally gave up and went to bed, lying in the dark, curled up in a lonesome, miserable knot of pain because of her inability to reach him.

She awakened the following morning to find herself alone in the cabin, a circumstance that was repeated on each successive morning. Where he slept was a subject she tried to keep from thinking about.

The return of the crew from their week off had supplied Phel with another reason to withdraw to a more discreet distance. It seemed to Gabe that he welcomed the cushioning effect Turk and Elmer provided. Their week of intimacy might never have been for all his coolness when the crew was present.

A sensible little voice persistently reminded her that he was only protecting her position in treating her in such a businesslike manner, and she would have been content with that had she enjoyed some intimacy with him in private. But he had determinedly seen to it that they spent no time alone together.

Unfortunately, Gabe's aching need for Phel's love wasn't dependent upon their being alone. The time spent with him in the others' presence only served to heighten her awareness of him. As she stood and watched him converse with Elmer, she was overwhelmed by a feeling of tenderness, almost losing her equilibrium as his endearing smile touched her heart.

It took all the strength and dignity she could muster to keep from acting like a silly schoolgirl in his presence. She had to still the urge to rhapsodize about him to everyone she talked to. With a sense of wonder, she realized that all the rapture of falling in love was just as intense as when she had been young and first in love with Buddie—maybe even more so.

And still, casting a pall over her soaring heart, was Phel's long silence. The painful uncertainty of recklessly giving one's heart was just as bewildering now as at any age. From time to time she surprised him, catching an unexpected affectionate glance that renewed her spirit, but still he said nothing and night after night passed without him coming to her.

The aching longing to be in his arms, to revel in his lovemaking, wasn't just a physical need but a reflection of her emotional attachment to him. Mind and body refused to work separately. As soon as she started thinking about him, her feelings were manifested by a throbbing need for the nearness of him.

Reminding herself that she was supposed to be working, Gabe wound up the long hose of the sprayer and carried it to the flatbed truck where all the equipment was kept when not in use. She had just finished putting away the spray shield and brushes when she heard Marlene hail her from the front porch of the A-frame.

"Gabe!" she called. "How about a coffee break?"

"Be right in," Gabe answered. She had intended to go in anyway to wash the paint thinner from her hands so it wouldn't irritate her delicate skin.

She stood at the little sink and lathered her hands and arms up to her elbows while Marlene poured mugs of hot, fragrant coffee. A platter of raisin-nut oatmeal cookies fresh from the oven teased Gabe's nostrils, making her realize she was hungry already even though it was only ten-thirty.

So much for the claim that being in love ruined your appetite, she thought. Unless, of course, what she felt for Phel Cannon was simply infatuation. Did that exhilarating but short-lived experience create a hunger for anything but a taste of the passion that prompted it?

"I've been dying to talk to you." Marlene plunged right into what was on her mind without waiting for Gabe to be seated. "I hope you won't think I'm just gossiping, but I'm only telling you this because I know you would never say anything to anyone else."

Gabe sat down at the table, pushing her hair back away from her face in a restless gesture. She was torn between her need to know about Phel—for she was sure that his marriage was the subject of Marlene's excitement—and the fear that she might betray a confidence he'd given her in a vulnerable moment.

She raised troubled eyes to study the younger girl. The eager look on Marlene's face was suddenly replaced by disappointment and indecision.

"Oh, you already know!" She faltered. "Please don't hate me for wanting to discuss it with you. You know how much I love Phel, and you know I'd never talk about him to just anybody."

Gabe drew in her breath, stunned by Marlene's words. But of course, she reminded herself cruelly, you knew she adored him the first minute after you met her. Why the big surprise now to hear her say it aloud?

"Isn't it risky?" Gabe inquired in a not-too-steady voice. "To fall in love with the man when you know the reason for his bitterness, his distrust of women?"

"Fall in love?" Marlene asked incredulously. "Me, fall in love?"

"But you just said—"

"You think I'm *in love* with Phel?" Marlene's tinkling giggle rang out, growing into a healthy laugh. Her peach-toned complexion was heightened as if someone had just brushed her cheeks with rouge.

"Oh, Gabrielle! He's the same age as my *father!*"

"He's a dynamic, handsome, sensual man!" Gabe bristled in defense. "Don't tell me you don't find him attractive!"

"Oh, sure." Marlene smiled. "I think he's terribly attractive . . . but not as a . . . sweetheart."

Gabe found herself sputtering in relief. "You . . . you haven't made yourself very clear, you know, saying you loved him."

"Oh, but I'd *never* . . . I mean, knowing that you and he . . ." Marlene blushed prettily. "Well, it's been pretty obvious that you and Phel . . ."

With sudden clarity Gabrielle could see what Marlene was too polite to put into words. For almost two months she and Phel had shared the intimate confines of this tiny cabin. Although their affair had begun only relatively recently, Marlene had obviously figured out what was going on, and her sense of fair play, if nothing else, would have kept her from poaching on another's territory, no matter what her own feelings might have been.

In a painfully revealing glimpse of her own ruthlessness where Phel was concerned, Gabrielle could see that no such sense of fair play would have kept her from doing whatever she had to do to win his love.

Just as quickly as the thought came it was followed by another. Why had she stood around wringing her hands for two whole weeks while their estrangement grew into an almost insurmountable barrier? Since when wasn't she ready and eager to go after what she wanted, no matter what the competition?

Maybe in this case the goal wasn't entry into the "good old boy's" club, or success in a nontraditional field. But the grit and determination to win her heart's desire would surely work for her just the same. Her tenacity had battered down the walls of a closed fraternity, gained her entry into the realm of builders. No one had eagerly welcomed her as an apprentice; they'd told her she couldn't do it. She had had to *prove* herself deserving of the rewards. She had had to work harder and longer than any of the men just to become accepted.

With determination strong within her, Gabrielle turned her attention to Marlene once more. "I want you to tell me everything you know about Phel and Amy's marriage," she directed.

The following discourse proved to be full of woefully few facts and a lot of supposition. After nearly half an hour Gabe felt that she actually knew no more than she had after the few brief sentences torn from Phel's lips when he'd confided in her out of desperation.

"The whole thing is really hard to understand." Marlene summed up her own frustration. "But maybe that's because we're looking at the affair from *our* perspective, how we perceive Phel as he is now."

"That's true," Gabe agreed. "It's difficult to imagine that any woman could forsake him for another man." She was glad she was seated, because weakness coursed through her at the thought of voluntarily giving up forever the excitement and wonder of sharing Phel's bed.

"My mother says it would be like expecting a girl to choose between some boy halfway through college, with hardly any prospects for the future, and Phel Cannon the way we know him: wealthy, successful."

Sensual, seductive . . . Gabe went on with the list in her mind. If Phel's long-absent father had been anything like his devastatingly handsome son was now, it wasn't too hard to figure out why Phel's fickle wife had succumbed to him.

"My mother says she thinks Amy being so impressed with Brock Cannon's worldliness and success probably caused Phel's own compulsion to succeed—to emulate his father."

"He certainly managed to do that," Gabe mused, almost to herself. "But how much satisfaction was there in surpassing his father's accomplishments if the end result was a desire to seclude himself on this island?"

"Oh, I don't think Phel ever meant to do that!"

"Then why would he choose to build here?"

"Maybe because he owned the property."

"But I assumed he bought it specifically to build on." Gabe's puzzlement was evident in her voice.

"From what I understand, he moved into the A-frame the winter Amy left because it was so cheap to live here," Marlene said. "Then, during all the years he lived in California, he still came back to the cabin every chance he got."

Gabe looked around the room at the desk and easy chairs, and finally at the big bed with its cheery patchwork quilt. How much easier it was to reconcile Phel's easy occupancy of the cabin with its inexpensive but homey furnishings now that she knew it had been his for years. A sudden rush of tenderness enfolded her at the knowledge that he'd been willing to share, even if only temporarily, his home with her.

Perhaps the task of tearing down his bitter wall of self-imposed isolation wouldn't be as difficult as she had anticipated.

The change in Gabrielle's manner was so abrupt that she surprised even herself. Marlene's turquoise eyes glittered eagerly at the change in her demeanor.

"Marlene"—Gabe lowered her voice, even though they were alone in the cabin—"there are two things I want you to do for me."

At precisely five-thirty Gabe looked at her watch and then over her shoulder at the cabin door. Right on schedule, Marlene appeared in the doorway, waved to Gabe and hurried down to the dock.

Turning to Elmer and Turk, Gabe asked if they were ready to knock off for the day.

"You don't have to ask me twice," Elmer agreed readily. "I'm ready for a cold beer."

"Well, I think you deserve one. Both of you have earned a bonus."

Elmer and Turk looked at each other, then back at their boss, grinning expectantly. Gabe cast another look at the cabin, then extracted her billfold from her coverall pocket. She quickly withdrew two fifty-dollar bills, handing one to each of the men.

"Treat's on me, fellows." She smiled at them. "I want you to take off right now; just pick up a change of clothes and take it with you."

Throwing another glance at the dock, she added,

"Marlene is waiting for you. She'll take you into town in the Eagle and bring you back out in the morning."

"I don't know what prompted this, but who am I to argue with the boss?" Elmer asked. Without questioning the unexpected largesse, he stuffed the bill into his jeans pocket. "A night in town at a hotel sounds good after rooming with the Turkey all summer."

Gabe breathed a sigh of relief as the two men disappeared inside the trailer to grab their gear just as Phel approached from the cabin. He greeted Gabe casually, not stopping in his progress toward the dock, where Marlene was untying the mooring lines.

"Oh, Phel," Gabrielle called to him. "Can I see you for a moment, please?"

His reluctance to talk to her without the buffering presence of Elmer or Turk was written clearly on his face. For a breathless moment she thought he was going to refuse her request.

Could he see the uncertainty with which she'd approached him? If he walked away from her now, her scheming with Marlene would have gained her nothing.

Oh, why had she thought, after his weeks of silence, that she could just invite him to stay on the island alone with her so she could seduce him again? Hadn't he made it perfectly clear by his refusal to allow a minute alone with her that he no longer wished to continue their affair?

Waves of insecurity washed over Gabe, even though she managed to hold the smile on her face. Gaining some time alone with him meant everything to her. Even though her heart told her that she couldn't have misinterpreted Phel's desire for her, it would cost her more than pride would allow if she made any overture in front of the others and he refused her.

Once they were alone she would do anything—whatever proved necessary—to cross the chasm between them.

She wasn't asking for any commitment from him. She was willing to delay any final decisions regarding their relationship until the end of summer. All she wanted now—in fact, desperately needed—was to end the separation that had cost her so many sleepless nights of longing.

"Well?" Phel prodded, coming closer.

Gabe cast a desperate glance at the dock, where Marlene still waited, then at the trailer, hoping Turk and Elmer would remain out of sight for a minute more.

The timing had to be perfect.

"I need to talk to you about the fireplace." Gabe watched as his gaze moved to the side of the log house where the huge basalt-rock fireplace had just been completed by the stonemasons.

"Can it wait until morning?" he asked, almost impatiently. "Marlene is waiting for me to take her home."

"I'd like you to check this so I can get my paperwork done tonight." Gabe was resolute. "You know how these subcontractors are. They want to get paid the minute they finish a job."

She turned and started up the path to the outside stairs leading up to the new deck, and was gratified to hear his footsteps behind her. After sliding open the glass door, she stepped into the dim interior. Once he'd entered she slid the door closed and flipped the latch, hoping he wouldn't notice her action.

She chattered about the quality of the work the masons had done, asking Phel if he approved of the placement of the stone shelves meant to display his bronzes. As though on cue, Gabe heard the roar of the Eagle's engines cut through the quiet evening. Phel turned in surprise, stepping to the broad picture window that offered a view of the dock and the lake.

Gabrielle almost purred in satisfaction at how well timed her plans had been. Turning toward the fireplace once more, she extended a hand in invitation. "They're gone," she said boldly. "So now you don't have to hurry."

Sitting down on the stone ledge of the new hearth, she unlaced her boots and then stood up to shuck off her coveralls. A snug-fitting black knit jumpsuit was all she wore beneath her rugged work clothes.

Comprehension dawning at last, Phel looked around at the heavy quilt spread on the rough floorboards before the crackling fire. A pile of pillows, a picnic hamper and a bottle of wine cooling in an icebucket awaited them.

"About this fireplace," he said gruffly, still reluctant to succumb to her wiles.

"About this fireplace," Gabe repeated. "It's ready for initiation." She swayed against him provocatively and heard his breath catch as she sank against his stiffly protesting frame. "A fireplace of such magnificence surely deserves a momentous launching, with fine food . . . and wine . . . and lovemaking.''

"Gabrielle," he moaned into her hair. "Gabrielle, my sweet." His hands pulled her closer, reading the response of her hardened nipples and heaving breasts against his chest. "How do you expect me to think of food and wine at a time like this?" he asked, his voice already hoarse with his rising passion.

As one, they sank to the cushioning pile of pillows, already heedless of the crackling fire or the growing darkness of the unfinished room. All her aching need to hold him close threatened to overcome Gabe, and she thought she would drown in her desire for him.

Her fingers worked at loosening the buttons of his shirt and when she laughed huskily at her shaking ineptitude he pulled the buttons apart from their holes, uncaring that one snapped from its thread and bounced across the floor.

"Phel, Phel . . ." she crooned, her lips against his face. "I've never wanted or needed any man like I want you. I've been going crazy with wanting you."

His kiss stilled her soft complaint, searing her moistly parting lips, both of them rejoicing in the reunion. Her heart thumped wildly, carrying the fever through her blood. Through the thin material of her jumpsuit she could feel his hands lighting similar fires. How her flesh ached for his caress! If only he could touch her everywhere at once.

Shifting slightly, he covered her legs with his own strong thigh, a pleasurable weight that she bore willingly. As though of its own volition her body lifted to meet his, inviting him to rest in the cradle of time, to replenish his soul and spirit at the trough of love.

Suddenly her clothing became an unbearable restraint, a barrier that kept her from delighting in the closeness she desired. As though he read her mind, his hands found the long nylon zipper and pulled it down. Slipping aside the satiny fabric he looked for long moments at the patterns the dancing flames cast over her body. His fingers lovingly traced the outline of her tanned shoulder, softly touching the skin where it became milky white.

Her breasts felt full, straining to meet his hands as he cupped them, buried his face in her warm flesh. His tongue was a dagger of fire, outlining each mounded orb, tracing the puckering edge of the nipple. His teeth were savagely gentle as they seized the rosebuds, teasing first one and then the other until she cried out.

"Must you torture me so?"

His answer was a moan, a gruff, masculine sound deep in his throat. A thrill surged through her in reply to the sound of an animal that must have its mate.

Oh, God! I love him, her heart cried silently. The words would have sprung involuntarily from her lips but his mouth again held hers captive, smothering them until they were only a muffled, unintelligible whimper.

With an easy motion he raised her hips to remove her garment, sliding it easily down over her silken thighs. She could feel the heat of the fire's dancing flames on her flesh, along with a glow from within that drove away the chill of the evening as his hands moved up and down her trembling legs until, at last, he parted them.

She took his weight easily, cradling him in her arms as they rocked together to the rhythm of passion. She couldn't quiet the soaring spiral of passion, nor did she want to slow their progress toward that magical release.

Reaching that exquisite plane together, they clutched each other convulsively, crying out in their ecstasy, almost sobbing at the intensity of their rapture.

For a long time after they were silent. When at length Phel stirred to nestle Gabrielle's head more comfortably against him, she sighed.

"Don't push me away again, Phel." Her voice was soft and plaintive. "I couldn't bear to sleep alone again tonight."

His deep chuckle came as a surprise. "You've left me no choice, conniving female that you are. You not only got rid of all our company, you sent away my bed as well."

"What do you mean?"

"The Eagle." He laughed softly. "Where do you think I bunk on the nights I force myself to stay away from your bed?"

"I hadn't figured it out," she admitted. "All I knew was that I was missing you, longing for you."

"Tonight neither of us will have to do that," he promised huskily.

And just for that night Gabe was willing to accept that and not ask about the days to come.

Shaking her head as the salesman displayed still another swatch of upholstery fabric, Gabrielle turned to Phel. "I must be hard to please, but I just haven't seen anything that genuinely complements the elegance of the house's lines. Of course, it's your decision, but I'm disappointed in what we've seen so far."

"I agree. Let's take a break and look some more after lunch."

After thanking the salesman for his patience, Phel held the door open for Gabe as she stepped out onto the sidewalk.

"How many more furniture stores are there in Kalispell?" Her question held more resignation than eagerness.

"A couple," Phel said with just as little enthusiasm, ushering her into a restaurant.

When the waitress had taken their order Gabe sat back in the tall booth and looked around at the high ceilings and old photographs decorating the interior of the health-food restaurant.

"I guess I could try to make a trip to Spokane or Seattle," Phel offered. "But I really am relying on you to help me select furnishings that go well with what you've already chosen."

Pleased that he approved of her decorating scheme for the interior, Gabe wondered briefly if she could afford to leave the crew to complete the finish work while she went off on a shopping spree with Phel. Much as the idea appealed to her, she felt that her presence was needed to insure that the work was completed on time.

"I haven't had a chance to tell you yet." Phel reached across the table to cover one of Gabe's hands with his own. "But I'm planning an open house for the week after the completion date. I've already invited some influential people from various parts of Montana."

Gabe's mouth formed an O as she considered the news. She'd frequently wished that the house weren't in such an isolated location so she could use it as a reference with prospective customers.

As though reading her thoughts, Phel went on, "I'll be surprised if you don't pick up some prospects from the guest list I've compiled. I kept that in mind when I made up the list."

"It would be super if I got another contract around here!" She was delighted with the idea. "The only other bid I might be in the running for right now is in Colorado."

"If you get it, will you be going there yourself, or will you just send a crew?"

"I'm afraid my business isn't big enough yet to allow me to just do the bidding and architectural refining, then send someone else to do the work. Maybe someday I can afford to do that, but until then I plan to keep on swinging the hammer, right alongside the rest of the crew."

"No matter where it takes you?" he asked gruffly.

"Anywhere that's profitable."

"So money is everything!"

"No, it's not everything," she said quickly, knowing somehow that he was thinking of Amy's craving for financial security. "But it seems to me it's always those who have more than enough money who denigrate its importance."

Thankful for the interruption provided by the arrival of their food, Gabe changed the subject. "Have you considered buying some antiques?"

"What sort of antiques?" He too seemed anxious to put their disagreement behind them. "The storage area behind the A-frame is full of antiques."

Gabe wrinkled her nose as she laughed. "I'm sure some of that rusty iron is old enough to qualify, but I don't think it's what you want to adorn a new house."

"What are you thinking of, then?"

"It just seems to me that all the furniture we've seen is from the wrong century. Why don't we look in some of the antique stores and see if we can find a few choice pieces to use as a base, and then build around them to furnish the house."

Her excitement was catching. Phel's imagination began to grasp her idea and work with it. "I know just where to start!" he exclaimed. "We'll go over as soon as we finish eating."

"Well, I hope you can wait long enough for me to order a slice of that huckleberry cream cheese pie for dessert," Gabe teased.

Before the afternoon was over they had visited a half-dozen antique stores and selected one or more pieces of furniture for each room of the house.

Trusting her natural instinct for overall integration, Gabe was sure that furniture from a more elegant era, rather than the starkly modern options of the present, would extend the aura of the house's rustic and yet timeless design all through its interior. She could sense Phel's approval after they'd found a round oak dining-room table, chairs and a hutch. Only carefully selected upholstery fabric for the chairs was needed to refurbish the set to perfect condition.

Gabe blushed modestly under Phel's teasing leer

as the slender, schoolmarmish shop owner extolled the virtues of an oversized sleigh bed, inviting Gabe to lie down on the bed and try it to see how comfortable it was.

Wishing it really mattered if she found the bed to her liking, Gabe went along with the sales pitch and stretched languorously on the quilted bedcover. Phel grinned wolfishly, telling the shopkeeper that it would take a bed of that dimension to accommodate the two of them comfortably.

As he wrote a check and made arrangements for delivery, Gabe wondered how few, if any, nights she might have to savor the pleasure of sharing the sleigh bed with Phel before her work was finished and she had no reason to linger.

At least now she would be given a one-week grace period between the completion and the open house. Since Phel had asked her to coordinate the interior design and check up on delivery of his purchases and other details to insure that the house was ready for the big party he had planned, she was sure she would have plenty to do to justify her staying behind when the crew left.

And then . . .

Why couldn't she simply be content with the knowledge that Phel had asked her to spend another week with him? Would he have insisted she stay around for the open house if he weren't concerned at least a little about her future?

It would be better for her mental health, she knew, not to mention her disposition, if she could just accept each day without agonizing over how many more she had left to spend with Phel.

But how would she be able to stand it if she

continued to deceive herself into a state of tranquility, only to find after the housewarming that his interest in her had only been physical? What if he found it easy to say, "So long, it's been a great summer?"

How could she bear it if . . . ? Oh, there were so many unanswerable questions to torture herself with.

Pushing aside her fears, she asked Phel what he thought of a magnificent armoire she had spotted just inside a door marked "Employees Only."

"Oh, that just came in," the shopkeeper hastened to explain. "I'd love to sell it to you, but it needs some repairs on the hinges and I'll have to find a mirror of the same vintage to replace that one, because it's in deplorable condition."

"That's all right." Phel drew out his checkbook from his vest pocket once more. "I can give you until the first week in September to have it ready for delivery."

With a flustered look on her face and dollar signs in her eyes, the proprietress named an outrageous figure. Phel wrote out the check with a flourish and handed it to her.

"Well . . . thank you, Mr . . ." She cast a quick look down at the check in her hand. "Mr. Cannon. It's a pleasure doing business with you. And with you, Mrs. Cannon."

Outside, Gabrielle caught Phel's arm. "You could have bargained for a better price," she said. "She would have taken a much lower offer, I'm sure."

"Don't you like it?"

That was hardly the point, Gabe thought. "Of

course *I* like it. That's why I suggested you look at it, but—"

"Then if you like it, it's worth the price, so don't nag—*Mrs.* Cannon."

Gabe tried to smile and make a joke in answer to his, but her knees were shaking and a funny little chill raced along her spine, so she just muttered under her breath about domineering men and started toward the car.

In a shop specializing in oak they chose bathroom and kitchen accessories in keeping with the furnishings. Gabe thought it was amazing how much simpler the task of interior decoration had become once the few core pieces had been selected.

A final stop on the edge of town proved to be a treasure trove. The purchase of a large oak library table with waterfall design drawers, along with several occasional tables and chairs, left them both feeling heady with elation.

The shop owner was ready to close when Gabe discovered a dainty blue velvet couch she found irresistible.

"If you don't buy it I'll get it for myself," she proclaimed. At Phel's obvious reluctance she added, "You still have three empty rooms. The den and two guest rooms."

"I've decided to have some of my old office furniture, which is stored in Los Angeles, shipped up for the den."

"Knowing you, it's massive and masculine," she reminded him. "Not that I'm saying there's anything wrong with that, but someday in the future you might . . ."

She left the words unsaid, not able to say out loud that someday he might decide to share his home and wish it contained at least a few feminine touches.

"You're right, of course." He smiled warmly. "Forgive me for asking you to assume the task and then not listening to your advice."

The store's owner, in true entrepreneurial spirit, hurried to suggest that a delightful Louis XIV bedroom set in the display window was precisely what was needed to complement the velvet divan.

His indulgent smile suggested that, after all, lovers should always strive to please each other. "I'm positive that you, sir, and you, madame, will never regret the compromise you have made. You will both enjoy these lovely furnishings for many, many years."

Oh, how Gabrielle wished there were some way his prophecy might come true!

It was already dark when they left Kalispell. They'd gone less than ten miles south when Phel pulled off the highway into a parking lot in front of a block-long resort complex. Blinking neon signs invited travelers to satisfy their hunger, thirst and need for rest in the sprawling building.

"They serve a fabulous chuck-wagon buffet here, and I think a celebratory drink is in order."

Gabe was hungry and more than willing to postpone the hour-long drive back to the island. She wanted only to hold on to the intimacy she'd so recently regained with Phel, and to enjoy a little longer the lovely fantasy that shopping with him had created.

He held her elbow solicitously as they climbed a

broad staircase carpeted in lush red. As they entered the restaurant she resisted the temptation to lean back into the circle of his arm.

By common consent they relaxed over a carafe of Beaujolais before joining the line of people filling their plates with tempting food at the salad bar and buffet. Protesting that she couldn't possibly eat so much, Gabe watched as the white-hatted chef carved slices of rare prime rib and heaped them on her plate.

She was feeling the effects of the wine and basking in the rosy glow of a successful day. When they reached their secluded table she impulsively gestured for Phel to sit next to her on the banquette rather than across the table, as he had earlier.

She turned to brush her lips against his as he lowered himself onto the seat beside her. The casual touch became a magnetic connection that neither of them could break. His arm came around her shoulder and drew her up against him. She could feel his warm breath against her cheek as they sat silently for a few minutes.

"We should try to eat a little," he ventured at last, his voice husky with the words he wasn't saying. Gabe nodded mutely and picked up her fork. She had managed to force down a few bites when his hand found her knee and strayed up and down her inner thigh, teasing the flesh through the thin fabric of her cotton dress.

Turning to him, she looked up through thick, silky lashes. "Who'd ever think it would be such torture to try to eat such a wonderful meal?" she asked with no coyness in her manner.

"Sometimes a man has to decide what his

priorities are," Phel answered as he rose and dropped his napkin on the white tablecloth. "Don't go away."

Before she could protest he had reached the staircase and was descending to the lobby. Playing with her salad, but not really eating it, she waited the few minutes until he returned.

He walked up to the table and tossed several large bills next to his plate, then held out his hand to her.

It was only a few steps down a discreetly lit hallway to the room he had secured. Almost before the door closed behind them they fell on the bed together, crying out their need for one another.

At the moment of release Gabe called out Phel's name, shuddering in ecstasy as he joined her in that brief paradise. "Oh, Phel! Phel, I love you so much."

Gathering her in his arms, he stilled her trembling, pressing warm, tender kisses to her brow. At last he spoke.

"Sweet Gabrielle. You're so intoxicating." Her heart thundered painfully against her ribs as she realized that she'd at last given voice to the words she'd suppressed so often before.

"I just can't get enough of you." The words were husky with passion. But in spite of the warmth inside the circle of his arms, Gabe felt a little chill move along her spine.

He hadn't said he loved her.

The drive home was accomplished in what seemed like moments. Snuggled against Phel's shoulder, Gabe wondered if she'd fallen asleep, because the time had passed so quickly.

The wind seemed ever-present on the surface of the lake at night. The chilling breeze soon robbed her of whatever warmth she'd felt in the car as Phel rowed across the inlet to the island. She was further chilled by his words.

"I'm going to be leaving early in the morning," he said in an unemotional tone. "Probably before you get up. If it's all right with you I'll just leave you some credit cards and a few signed checks in case you find something for the house while I'm away."

"How long will you be gone?" Her voice rose in anxious uncertainty. She felt shrewish for asking; she didn't really have the right to expect an explanation from him.

How could he go? Her heart lunged in sudden fear of the truth. How could he leave her now when there was so little time left until the house was finished?

"Probably about a week." He smiled down at her. "If I'm lucky I should have everything wrapped up by then. And," he added with an affectionate squeeze of her arm, "I have to get back in time for the open house, don't I?"

In spite of the queasy feeling in her stomach, Gabe forced a smile. In time for the open house. But that was two weeks away! How could she bear it if he were gone for the rest of the time she had left on Wild Stag Island?

10

Gabrielle stepped out of the shower and reached for a thick white bath towel. Looking around the luxurious new bathroom at the oak and brass fixtures, she experienced a rush of well-being. Not only did she feel the satisfaction of having brought together all the elements that contributed to the classy style of the room, but after months of living with the A-frame's lack of amenities, she relished the convenience and comfort she now enjoyed.

Even though most of the furniture had been delivered, she continued to sleep in the A-frame, cherishing the tenuous link it gave her with Phel; yet she found the small cabin unbearably empty without him.

After slipping into jeans and a crisp gray-and-white pin-striped blouse, she blew her hair dry. It had grown almost to shoulder length during the summer and been lightened a shade by her many hours in the sun. Even though she felt little incentive to primp, she smoothed on makeup and did her eyes just in case today proved to be the day Phel returned.

An hour later, with a hearty breakfast behind them, she helped Elmer and Turk load the camper trailer on the raft. Successive trips across the narrow inlet accomplished the task of removing all traces of the building crew's three-month-long occupancy.

"Are you sure you don't want us to tow the trailer with the truck and leave the pickup for you?" Elmer asked for the third time.

"No, it would be more help to me if you and Turk each drive one of the rigs back to Spokane, so I don't have to face a seven-hour drive when I've finished here." The very thought of leaving the island was something she couldn't deal with without getting choked up. "I have Phel's car to drive—or I can ride the cycle—so you don't have to worry about my being stranded. When I've finished up I'll just hitch a ride into Missoula with Marlene or . . . someone, and fly to Spokane."

Turk climbed into the old flatbed truck and revved the engine impatiently. "See you back in the city, boss lady," he called out. Gabe could tell that the young carpenter was more than willing to end his summer of isolation.

Looking embarrassed, Elmer offered his hand, and then pulled Gabe into an awkward but affectionate hug. "Now see here, Missy Gabe," he stammered. "You take care of yourself, you hear?"

Gabrielle beamed at him, pleased by his uncharacteristic show of affection. "I will, Elmer. Thank you. You guys have done a terrific job this summer."

When she entered the house she was greeted by Marlene's cheery voice. "Coffee?" she asked Gabe.

"No, thanks, I had more than enough at breakfast."

"Do you mind if I bring mine in to where you're working?"

"Not at all," Gabe responded, wondering what the cheerful brunette had on her mind. Marlene followed her into the living room and seated herself on the luxurious amber-colored velvet sofa that had been delivered the previous day.

"This room is just gorgeous," she sighed as Gabe began unpacking and dusting the bronze art collection. "What a wonderful home this will be—quite a change from the A-frame, isn't it?"

"Yes," Gabe agreed.

"I think it says something about the kind of person Phel is that he wasn't impatient with the A-frame during all the time it took to plan this house, and then all the months of negotiations and building."

Gabe cast a look of surprise at Marlene. "I've never considered patience one of Phel's virtues," she scoffed. "It seems to me that he wants what he wants when he wants it."

Marlene's laugh was tinkly and clear. "That's probably true in a lot of instances. He *can* be like a bear with a wounded paw."

Gabrielle stood on the hearth and stretched to place a Charles Russell bronze on the highest shelf,

170

then angled an unobtrusive spotlight to highlight the piece. When she turned to face Marlene again she noticed a look of indecision on the girl's face.

"All right," she said in a motherly tone. "Spit it out. I can see something is troubling you."

"Well, I have a message to deliver to you from Phel."

"It must be something pretty terrible if it has you that worried."

"It's just that I know you'll be disappointed," Marlene sighed. "I know you've practically been watching out the window for him to return all week. And now I have to tell you that he won't be here until next week."

Gabe could almost feel the color draining out of her face. "But the party . . ."

"He said to tell you not to worry, he'll be here in plenty of time for the open house."

"Did he say . . . anything else?" Gabe asked hopefully.

"I only talked to him for a minute after he talked to my mother for a while," Marlene said. "He asked us if we could handle putting away all the new things as they arrive so everything will be ready for the caterers."

"I hope you told him it was almost all done."

"Oh, yes. I really bragged about how much you've done and how neat the house looks already."

"He didn't say why he was detained?" Gabe ventured to ask, sensing sympathy in Marlene's eyes.

"Only that everything was going super well, but taking longer than he had expected."

"Well, then," Gabe assumed a false brightness, "I guess we'd better keep busy, since we aren't getting any help."

"Oh, we'll get all the help we need. You just tell me or Mother what you want done and we'll send someone out to do it."

"Thanks," Gabe replied. Suddenly all the luster of the day and all her pleasure in her beautiful surroundings had vanished.

It would be a whole week until he returned.

As Gabe went about the task of finishing the art display she couldn't keep one haunting thought out of her mind. When she left the island in a week, this emptiness and longing were what she would take with her—forever.

Rebecca Tennyson was a twenty-pound-heavier, twenty-year-older version of her daughter. If Gabe hadn't already felt she knew and liked Rebecca through her discussions with Marlene, she would have been charmed by her immediately anyway.

Arriving with Marlene in the Eagle on the morning of the open house, Rebecca had apron in hand and was prepared to move mountains if need be to have everything ready in time for the party that evening.

The three women worked together faultlessly, directing the catering people as they unloaded the van full of party ware after Gabe had brought them across on the raft.

Both Gabe and Marlene kept an anxious eye on the clock, although Rebecca assured them several times that watching wouldn't make the hands move any faster.

"Phel said he'd be here, so he'll be here."

The pealing of the doorbell brought all three women rushing from various parts of the house to answer it. Standing on the flagged entryway outside the door was Phel, hat in hand and a sheepish look upon his face.

"Would you believe I don't have a key to my own front door?"

"No one has used the front door yet," Marlene said tartly. "We peons all used the servants' entrance in the back."

With an affectionate grin Phel brushed past Marlene, greeted Rebecca with thanks for helping out and then turned to meet Gabe's flustered gaze.

"Welcome home," she breathed past a painful lump in her throat.

"Thank you, it's good to *be* home."

Before either one of them could speak further Rebecca interrupted to remind Phel that his first party guests would be arriving in just over an hour.

Looking ruefully down at his rumpled clothing, he brushed a hand across his bristly jaw. "You're right," he agreed. "I'll have to talk to you later. So much has happened. . . ." He raised his hand to touch Gabe's hair, but withdrew it quickly.

"I hope you have something smashing to wear tonight. I'm looking forward to having you act as hostess so you can reap the praise you deserve for the house."

"Yes," Gabe replied, glad that she'd planned ahead to cover the situation. "I picked up a new dress in Missoula the day I bought the couch."

"Oh! The couch!" Phel looked around for the first time. "Everything looks sensational."

"Thanks," Gabe mumbled, turning away so he wouldn't see her disappointment at the casual reunion. She had only taken a few steps down the hall when he overtook her. Without a word he swept her into his arms and kissed her soundly. Only Gabe's protesting "Ouch!" could have ended the kiss so easily.

"Sorry, I forgot." He rubbed his whiskery chin again. "Just glad to see you. I've got a lot to tell you, but I guess it will have to wait."

With a lilting song on her lips to buoy her steps, Gabrielle let herself out the door and went to the A-frame to get ready for the party.

The merit of passive solar heating was a topic Gabrielle never tired of discussing. Ned Blakely, the earnest young architect she was conversing with, showed every bit as much enthusiasm for the subject, or perhaps he was willing to discuss anything that interested the tall, willowy contractor as long as she remained at his side.

Gabe cast a sweeping look around the crowded room and finally spotted Phel in the overflow of guests seated at the wooden tables scattered about on the huge deck. Discovering that he was intent upon a discussion with two tall, well-dressed older men, she returned her attention to her companion of the moment.

". . . that's why the roof overhang is so important," the architect was saying. "Otherwise, the windows that provide the welcome warmth of the sun in winter would make it unbearably hot in the summer."

A feeling of sadness swept over Gabrielle, shadowing her countenance as she thought that she wouldn't be around to see the benefits of the changes she'd made in Phel's original house plans to make use of passive solar energy. Listening only halfheartedly, she nodded as Ned went on with his recitation.

Suddenly aware that Ned was staring at her as though expecting a response, Gabe gave herself a mental shake and looked up. "I'm sorry," she apologized. "I'm afraid I have a lot on my mind."

"I said I don't really want to introduce you to this guy, but he won't stop hanging around listening to our conversation until I do." He gestured toward a nattily dressed, blond Viking at his side.

"Marshall Haymes, this vision of loveliness is the person responsible for this magnificent dwelling."

Gabe extended her hand and looked up to meet twinkling blue eyes. "How nice to meet you."

"Marshall is an attorney for the power company that laid the cable under the lake," Ned explained.

Before Gabe could utter an acknowledgment, her hand was grasped firmly. A quick tug brought her almost up against Phel.

"I don't blame you fellows for flocking around the most beautiful woman in the territory," he grumbled goodnaturedly. "But unless you want to contract her services to build a house for you, she doesn't have time to talk to you right now."

He retained his grip on her hand and started to move away from Ken and Marshall. From the look on his face, Gabe couldn't tell if Phel were serious or only teasing.

"I guess I'll see you later," she said over her shoulder to the two men.

Pausing only briefly to greet several guests who had arrived late, Phel continued to propel her until they reached a small table next to the railing of the deck. The two men Phel had been talking to earlier rose to greet her as they approached.

Phel made quick introductions. "Dell is in the governor's office," he explained. "And Hugh is Polson's best bowler and a pretty fair dentist to boot."

The two men insisted that Gabe sit down so they could ask her about her career as a builder and more particularly about some of the most outstanding features of Phel's home.

"I can't believe anyone as glamorous as you could possibly swing as mean a hammer as Phel claims!" Hugh exclaimed.

Gabe was pleased but a little embarrassed at the extravagant praise. She drew the line a little short of thinking herself glamorous, although she knew the smart new amber velvet two-piece dress she wore made the most of her honeyed tan and lit butterscotch-colored highlights in her hazel eyes.

Excusing himself to make the rounds of his guests, Phel left Gabrielle laughing with pleasure at the flattery of the two gallant older men.

"I'd be happy to start on a new cabin if I thought it would keep a beauty like you here at Flathead Lake for a few more months," the courtly Hugh said. "I might even give up a couple of my bowling leagues so I could be around to help you build it."

"I'll be happy to build your home for you," Gabe responded sweetly. "But I don't hire any scabs, so I can't use your help. My crews are all union carpenters."

The party had slowed down considerably by the time Gabe and her two companions moved indoors. Only a few straggling guests still chatted in comfortable little groups, the rest having been ferried across to the dock by two of the caterer's men.

"Both your conquests regretfully asked me to convey their farewells and the hopes of seeing you again," Phel said with a distinct lack of humor. "I can see I was wise to sidetrack you with these two harmless old blowhards."

"Hey, wait a minute," Hugh protested. "There's nothing harmless about either one of us. We're both prepared to sign contracts tomorrow just to keep Gabrielle here long enough to see if we can take her away from you."

"Now, I could never allow that." Phel draped a proprietorial arm about her shoulders. "Not even for the most lucrative contract."

The sputter of outboard motors died abruptly when the raft carrying the last of the party guests reached the opposite shore, leaving only the methodical chirping of crickets to break the night silence.

Phel's arm about Gabrielle's waist remained in place, even after they'd waved to the retreating raft for the last time. With a little squeeze he guided her toward the door and the warmly lit living room.

Not a glass nor an ashtray had been left by the caterers to mark the passing of nearly a hundred guests. To Gabe's surprise, the living room was just as spotless as it had been before the party started.

To her chagrin, she realized that she'd been so

absorbed in her talk with Hugh and Dell about possible building projects that she hadn't even noticed when Marlene and her mother had left, nor thanked all the others whose attendance had made Phel's housewarming such a success.

"I guess I haven't been a very solicitous hostess," she apologized. "See how I am when business intrudes on pleasure?"

"Yes, you're a real shark, aren't you?" His voice was husky with affection.

"It's just that . . . well, if I have another house to build . . ." Gabrielle's eyes seemed enormous in her face. The shadows beneath them were evidence of her past two weeks of tension and distress.

But now she had an appointment to meet first with Hugh, and later with Dell, in Polson, so she could show them a selection of plans. Of course, setting things up took time—sometimes months to complete contractual obligations. And then it would be winter. So, realistically, she mustn't get her hopes up. It could be as long as six months before she could actually begin work on another house here in Montana.

Six months! And where would Phel be in that length of time? And how could she bear to go through six months without him? The last two weeks had been a torture she never wanted to endure again. Perhaps it would be better to just go away and make the break permanent, even though something within her would surely die.

"Let's forget about the house for a while," Phel said as he went around the room switching off all the lamps until there was only the soft glow from the fireplace. "I've been away too long to want to spend the rest of the night talking shop talk."

Gabrielle's breath went from her as he pulled her into his arms and kissed her long and deep. As their lips met in sweet reunion she pushed aside the unhappiness that threatened to overwhelm her if she allowed herself to remember that this would be the last night she would spend in Phel's arms for a long, long time—perhaps forever.

Gently and sweetly at first, they loved each other as the fire's glow cast dancing shadows on their naked skin. And then, like the fire, their passion flared until it consumed them totally.

"I've missed you immeasurably," Phel whispered against Gabe's shoulder as they lay in each other's arms afterward.

"You were gone an eternity." She tried to keep the hurt out of her voice. "The last week especially seemed endless."

"I'm sorry you got stuck with seeing to all the details before the open house."

Gabrielle bit back her protest, thinking it might be wise to allow him to go on thinking she was talking about his absence as an inconvenience rather than the painful loss that it had actually been.

It wouldn't do now, on the eve of her departure, to let him see how much it would hurt her to end their summer affair.

"Nothing could have kept me away for so long if it hadn't been imperative that I be there for a few more days."

Gabe turned slightly to make herself more comfortable and waited for him to go on.

"I feel kind of silly making such a mystery of everything, but I didn't know how successful I'd be in accomplishing my purpose when I left here. All I had was determination on my side."

Gabe thought briefly of what Marlene had said about Phel's patience in getting what he wanted. Determination, too, played a big part in gaining one's desires. A little smile tugged at the corner of her mouth. Hadn't he conquered her own resistance with his determination?

"After the day we spent horseback riding in the Swan Valley, I knew I would have to resolve some of the negative feelings I've carried around with me for the last eighteen years," Phel said. "I'd thought for a long time that if I had everything else I wanted, it wouldn't matter so much that I'd lost the big one."

Gabe was silent, thinking how calmly he talked of that episode in his life. He'd been wild with rage and pain the last time those old wounds had been uncovered.

"I set out to track my father down," Phel said huskily. "I found it's a little easier when you have money and social standing to aid in the search than it was when I was a teenager without family or other resources."

"It only took me a week to find out that my father had remarried and was living in a suburb of Chicago. But when I arrived there he was away on a business trip—not expected back until day before yesterday."

"So you only spent a day or two with him!"

Phel's arm tightened about Gabrielle's waist.

"That was enough, at least for this visit." Before Gabe could wonder whether his meeting with Brock Cannon hadn't gone well, he went on.

"I spent most of the days while I was waiting for him to return with my mother-in-law, a pudgy, energetic lady in her late fifties. She told me lots of things I never knew about my father. And she told me how he'd raised her three sons after he married her. How he always longed for me—his own son—but said at least there was some satisfaction in knowing he'd prevented her boys from suffering a fatherless childhood."

Phel's voice was deep with emotion. "He always wanted to come back here and make things square with me, but he was convinced I could never forgive him. Even with Muriel's help, it took me two days to convince him that my anger and outrage had always been directed at Amy, rather than at him."

"But he went away with her. . . ."

"Honey, in less than six months some *other* man went away with her. I've known for a long time that she wasn't much of a loss!"

"But still . . ."

"But still I managed to convince my father that if I could forgive and understand how he had been flattered by the attentions of a pretty young girl until he lost his head and gave in to her seduction attempts, then it was time for him to forgive himself for not having the strength to resist her."

Sighing deeply, Gabrielle nestled her head against Phel's shoulder. "I can't tell you how glad I am that you've healed all those old hurts. I only think it's a shame you had to hurry back here without spending more time together."

"That was easy to do, knowing Dad and Muriel would be coming out here in two weeks."

"So soon? That's wonderful! If I haven't finished negotiating the contracts with Dell and Hugh, I might be back over here in time to meet them."

"Of course you'll be here to meet them, my sweet Gabrielle. They're making the trip to attend our wedding."

So stunned that she couldn't reply, Gabe held her breath, not believing she'd heard him correctly. "But . . ." She found her voice at last.

"But surely you expect your prospective in-laws to attend your wedding," he prompted.

"Wedding! What are you talking about, Phel Cannon?" She rolled over and sat up. "Just because we let ourselves get carried away this summer doesn't mean we have to put our brains on the shelf for the winter too.

"You know I want a man who's gentle and thoughtful. I could never live with a man who's overbearing and autocratic. And you couldn't stand my independence for a week."

"Now when was the last time you saw me being overbearing?" The firelight reflected a twinkle in his dark blue eyes.

Gabe thought for a minute before she replied. "I guess it was the night I got here."

"Before I kissed your sweet lips or held your luscious body in my arms."

"You've come on plenty strong a few times since then!"

"You mean when Turk cast a lascivious eye on

182

the boss? Or when that overgrown logger had his hands on you?"

Gabrielle could feel the lump of pain that had been lodged in her throat for weeks dissolving. "But I'm used to making my own decisions . . . doing as I please, running my own business."

"Well, don't expect *me* to help you on that! I *am* retired, you know."

A tiny look of hope came alive in her eyes.

"Gabrielle, the very first thing that impressed me about you was the fact that you stood up for yourself and didn't lean on anybody. I couldn't stand a woman who was a clinging vine, who needed a man's support."

"But, then, why did you yell and curse at me? Try to make me go away just because I'm a woman?"

"For God's sake, Gabrielle! Couldn't you see even then that I couldn't keep my hands off you? I had to give you a chance to save yourself. How was I supposed to maintain the businesslike relationship you were demanding with you sleeping six feet away from my bed?"

"Don't you think that somewhere along the line we could have gotten a little communication going?"

The corner of his mouth twitching in dry humor, he replied, "We did manage to get a *little* communication going, even though you weren't prepared to listen to anything I wanted to tell you." Gently he settled Gabe back into his arms again.

"I wasn't willing to ask you to stay here in such an isolated area if your building career meant so much to you. It just took a while for me to get my mind off making love to you long enough to realize that if you can build one log home here you might as well build a dozen." He chuckled deeply.

"Of course, I expect a finder's fee for any contracts you get from the open house, because the guests were selected very carefully with that in mind."

"Baloney!" Gabe shot back. "If I get any more jobs it will be because I did such a splendid piece of work on this house, not because anyone arranged it for me."

At Phel's hearty laugh she pulled loose, crossing her arms over her bare bosom. "Anyway, that still doesn't do away with all our differences," she protested.

"Whoever said lovers are supposed to be exactly alike?"

"No one, but . . ."

"But nothing!" Phel covered her protesting lips with a hard kiss that threatened to rekindle the embers of passion they'd so recently banked. "I love you too much to have you turn me down just because I'm not a dead ringer for the man you picked out when you were only sixteen years old. I know you loved Buddie, but he's gone. And I'm here. And I love you enough for both of us."

"But, Phel . . ."

"You might as well surrender, woman. I intend to hold you captive on this island until you can resist no longer. You might as well name a date so I can call my folks."

The words held so much pride and contentment that Gabe choked up, understanding how special that phrase was to the man who'd lived most of his life without parents.

"You haven't even asked me if I really care about you."

"I don't have to ask, Gabrielle. I knew for a long time before you did that we'd be everything to each other."

Sighing softly, she rose to her feet and pulled at his hand until he stood up and put his arms around her once more.

"I've been crying my heart out every night since we picked out that sleigh bed because I wouldn't ever get to share it with you."

"I bought it for you," he said tenderly. "Along with the blue velvet couch. I've had the wildest fantasies about making love to you on that couch."

Together they moved down the lushly carpeted hall to the darkness of the master bedroom. Phel switched on one small lamp and turned to gaze down on Gabrielle's upturned face.

"Oh, Phel." Gabe was awash with emotion. "I've tried so hard to hide my love for you."

"You don't ever have to do that, sweetheart," he said as he slid his hands down over her curving hips to linger on her silken thighs. "I want to hear, all night long and every day after, how much you love me."

"I love you. I love you," she crooned softly as she surrendered to the warmth of his embrace. With a swooping motion he picked her up and strode to the huge bed.

"You see this sleigh bed?" he asked, a gleam of mischief lighting his blue eyes.

"What about this bed?"

"It is a grand and magnificent bed. Surely it should be initiated with good food and wine and lovemaking."

"Oh, Phel," Gabrielle sighed against his neck. "How can you think of food or wine at a time like this?"

Silhouette Desire
15-Day Trial Offer
A new romance series that explores contemporary relationships in exciting detail

Six Silhouette Desire romances, free for 15 days! We'll send you six new Silhouette Desire romances to look over for 15 days, absolutely free! If you decide not to keep the books, return them and owe nothing.

Six books a month, free home delivery. If you like Silhouette Desire romances as much as we think you will, keep them and return your payment with the invoice. Then we will send you six new books every month to preview, just as soon as they are published. You pay only for the books you decide to keep, and you never pay postage and handling.

YOU'LL BE SWEPT AWAY
WITH SILHOUETTE DESIRE

$1.75 each

1 ☐ CORPORATE AFFAIR
James

2 ☐ LOVE'S SILVER WEB
Monet

3 ☐ WISE FOLLY
Clay

4 ☐ KISS AND TELL
Carey

5 ☐ WHEN LAST WE LOVED
Baker

6 ☐ A FRENCHMAN'S KISS
Mallory

7 ☐ NOT EVEN FOR LOVE
St. Claire

8 ☐ MAKE NO PROMISES
Dee

9 ☐ MOMENT IN TIME
Simms

10 ☐ WHENEVER I LOVE YOU
Smith

$1.95 each

11 ☐ VELVET TOUCH
James

12 ☐ THE COWBOY AND THE
LADY   Palmer

13 ☐ COME BACK, MY LOVE
Wallace

14 ☐ BLANKET OF STARS
Valley

15 ☐ SWEET BONDAGE
Vernon

16 ☐ DREAM COME TRUE
Major

17 ☐ OF PASSION BORN
Simms

18 ☐ SECOND HARVEST
Ross

19 ☐ LOVER IN PURSUIT
James

20 ☐ KING OF DIAMONDS
Allison

21 ☐ LOVE INTHE CHINA SEA
Baker

22 ☐ BITTERSWEET IN BERN
Durant

23 ☐ CONSTANT STRANGER
Sunshine

24 ☐ SHARED MOMENTS
Baxter

25 ☐ RENAISSANCE MAN
James

26 ☐ SEPTEMBER MORNING
Palmer

27 ☐ ON WINGS OF NIGHT
Conrad

28 ☐ PASSIONATE JOURNEY
Lovan

29 ☐ ENCHANTED DESERT
Michelle

30 ☐ PAST FORGETTING
Lind

31 ☐ RECKLESS PASSION
James

32 ☐ YESTERDAY'S DREAMS
Clay

38 ☐ SWEET SERENITY
Douglass

39 ☐ SHADOW OF BETRAYAL
Monet

40 ☐ GENTLE CONQUEST
Mallory

41 ☐ SEDUCTION BY DESIGN
St. Claire

42 ☐ ASK ME NO SECRETS
Stewart

43 ☐ A WILD, SWEET MAGIC
Simms

44 ☐ HEART OVER MIND West

45 ☐ EXPERIMENT IN LOVE Clay

46 ☐ HER GOLDEN EYES Chance

47 ☐ SILVER PROMISES Michelle

48 ☐ DREAM OF THE WEST
Powers

49 ☐ AFFAIR OF HONOR James

50 □ FRIENDS AND LOVERS
Palmer

51 □ SHADOW OF THE
MOUNTAIN Lind

52 □ EMBERS OF THE SUN
Morgan

53 □ WINTER LADY Joyce

54 □ IF EVER YOU NEED ME
Fulford

55 □ TO TAME THE HUNTER
James

56 □ FLIP SIDE OF YESTERDAY
Douglass

57 □ NO PLACE FOR A WOMAN
Michelle

58 □ ONE NIGHT'S DECEPTION
Mallory

59 □ TIME STANDS STILL
Powers

60 □ BETWEEN THE LINES
Dennis

61 □ ALL THE NIGHT LONG
Simms

62 □ PASSIONATE SILENCE
Monet

63 □ SHARE YOUR
TOMORROWS Dee

64 □ SONATINA
Milan

65 □ RECKLESS VENTURE
Allison

66 □ THE FIERCE GENTLENESS
Langtry

67 □ GAMEMASTER
James

68 □ SHADOW OF YESTERDAY
Browning

69 □ PASSION'S PORTRAIT
Carey

70 □ DINNER FOR TWO
Victor

71 □ MAN OF THE HOUSE
Joyce

72 □ NOBODY'S BABY
Hart

73 □ A KISS REMEMBERED
St. Claire

74 □ BEYOND FANTASY
Douglass

75 □ CHASE THE CLOUDS
McKenna

76 □ STORMY SERENADE
Michelle

77 □ SUMMER THUNDER
Lowell

78 □ BLUEPRINT FOR RAPTURE
Barber

SILHOUETTE DESIRE, Department SD/6
1230 Avenue of the Americas
New York, NY 10020

Please send me the books I have checked above. I am enclosing $_____
(please add 50¢ to cover postage and handling. NYS and NYC residents please add
appropriate sales tax.) Send check or money order—no cash or C.O.D.'s please.
Allow six weeks for delivery.

NAME _____

ADDRESS _____

CITY _____ STATE/ZIP _____

Enjoy your own special time with Silhouette Romances.

Send for 6 books today—one is yours <u>free</u>!

Silhouette Romances take you into a special world of thrilling drama, tender passion, and romantic love. These are enthralling stories from your favorite romance authors—tales of fascinating men and women, set in exotic locations all over the world.

Convenient free home delivery. We'll send you six exciting Silhouette Romances to look over for 15 days. If you enjoy them as much as we think you will, pay the invoice enclosed with your trial shipment. **One book is yours free to keep.** Silhouette Romances are delivered right to your door with never a charge for postage or handling. There's no minimum number of books to buy, and you may cancel at any time.

Silhouette Romances

READERS' COMMENTS ON SILHOUETTE DESIRES

"Thank you for Silhouette Desires. They are the best thing that has happened to the bookshelves in a long time."
—V.W.*, Knoxville, TN

"Silhouette Desires—wonderful, fantastic—the best romance around."
—H.T.*, Margate, N.J.

"As a writer as well as a reader of romantic fiction, I found DESIREs most refreshingly realistic—and definitely as magical as the love captured on their pages."
—C.M.*, Silver Lake, N.Y.

*names available on request